Acknowledgements

The project leading to this publication is part of a collaborative programme between CIRIA and the Concrete Society entitled *Concrete techniques – site operations*. It was carried out under contract by The Imperial College of Science Technology and Medicine and Taywood Engineering .

The report was written by Dr N. R. Buenfeld and Dr R. Yang of the Department of Civil and Environmental Engineering at Imperial College.

The project was carried out and the report prepared under the guidance of the following Steering Group members:

Mr R A McClelland (chair)	Alfred McAlpine Construction Ltd
Dr P Bamforth	Taywood Engineering
Mr S Crompton	Ready Mix Concrete (UK) Ltd
Mr R Cather	Arup Research and Development
Dr C Clear	Civil and Marine Slag Cement Ltd
Mr D S Leek	Mott MacDonald, Special Services Division
Mr J Frearson	Rugby Cement (formerly Messrs Sandbergs)
Mr G P Hammersley	Building Research Establishment Ltd
Dr T Harrison	Quarry Products Association
Dr C Hopkins	Wardell Armstrong
Mr N Loudon	Highways Agency
Dr E Kay	Sir William Halcrow and Partners
Mr L H McCurrich	FOSROC International Technology
Mr M Messham	Sir Alexander Gibb & Partners
Dr J B Newman	Imperial College of Science Technology and Medicine
Mr P Owens	Quality Ash Association
Mr P F Pallet	Training Consultant
Dr W Price	Sandberg Consulting Engineers
Mr R Roberts	Concrete Advisory Service
Mr G P Tilley	Gifford and Partners
Mr P Titman	Edmund Nuttall
Mr C Turton	Design Group Partnership
Mr M Walker	The Concrete Society
Mr P Woodhead	Department of the Environment, Transport and the Regions.

The Steering Group delegated review of the detailed development to the following specialist Technical Committee:

Mr R Cather (chair)	Arup Research & Development
Mr R Baldwin	Mott MacDonald
Mr G Hammersley	Building Research Establishment Ltd
Mr A Harrison	Rugby Cement
Dr C Hopkins	Wardell Armstrong
Mr L Parrott	British Cement Association
Mr P Titman	Edmund Nuttall.

CIRIA's research manager for this project was Dr B W Staynes.

Contributions made to this work by the following are gratefully acknowledged: Dr Colin Hills, Emeka Agbasi, Roy Baxter and Eleanor Tipping at Imperial College who helped with the SEM method development described in Section 5.1.2; Dr Phil Bamforth, David Cullen and Andrew Pearce of Taywood Engineering; and Dr Mamoud Sadegzadeh of Aston Materials Services Ltd who carried out the abrasion testing.

This project was funded by the Department of the Environment, Transport and the Regions, the Concrete Society and CIRIA's Core programme sponsors.

CIRIA, the Concrete Society and the authors gratefully acknowledge the support of these funding organisations, and the technical help and advice provided by the members of the steering group and by the many other individuals who were consulted. Contributions do not imply that individual funders necessarily endorse all views expressed in published outputs.

Executive summary

Curing is widely perceived as being an important factor in achieving durable concrete structures. This seems reasonable in that curing allows hydration of cement to continue which is expected to reduce capillary porosity, thereby strengthening the concrete and increasing its resistance to penetration by aggressive agents such as chloride, sulphate and carbon dioxide. However, direct evidence that the levels of curing achieved on-site increases durability is scarce.

This report describes the second phase of an investigation into the influence of practical on-site curing on the durability of concrete. The first phase was a literature review (CIRIA PR49 by Hammersley et al, 1997), which arrived at limited conclusions concerning the effects of site curing on durability. The review also concluded that it was extremely unlikely that any currently established laboratory or site test method could form the basis of the assessment of on-site curing over the range of environmental exposures. The Project steering group for this second phase concluded that the assessment of curing effectiveness and its influence on durability performance could be most beneficially determined by considering the microstructure of the concrete in the curing affected zone (CAZ). This is the zone of concrete near to and including its outer surface, which can be directly affected by active external curing measures.

The objective of this second phase of the project was primarily to establish the viability of a method for investigating the link between practical curing methods and the micro-structure of concrete in the CAZ. A further objective was to investigate the relationship between microstructure in the CAZ and durability performance.

How should concrete microstructure be characterised? The limited literature suggested that, under some conditions, the CAZ is limited to a depth of only a few millimetres. It was therefore decided that a microscopy-based technique could be appropriate in that it would allow differences over small distances to be examined. To enable these to be quantified necessitated image analysis. The approach adopted to characterise concrete microstructure was therefore to obtain images of the concrete using scanning electron microscopy (SEM) and then to convert these images into microstructural parameters using computer-based image analysis.

In a "backscattered electron image" produced by the SEM (see Section 5.1.1 and Appendix A2 for a background to SEM), polished surfaces of concrete show at least five distinct phases according to their brightness (greyscale).

1. Porosity.

2. Calcium silicate hydrate gel.

3. Aggregate.

4. Calcium hydroxide.

5. Anhydrous cement.

The two phases of most interest were porosity (because of its link with durability) and anhydrous cement (closely linked to degree of hydration, the parameter most directly characterising the degree of curing).

Preliminary work was undertaken to develop the SEM method and to demonstrate that differences in porosity and anhydrous cement content could be identified and quantified (see Section 5.1.2). This involved determining the optimal magnification ($\times 500$) and other SEM and image analyser variables, developing methods of automatically collecting images at predefined positions on a specimen, separating the aggregate from the cement paste by image analysis, and determining the number of images required to produce statistically acceptable results.

The method was then applied in a large test programme executed over a 12-month period. Ten concrete test panels, measuring 1 m $\times 0.5$ m $\times 0.15$ m, of four different concretes (two of them including PFA or GGBS) were cured in up to four different ways and were subjected to nine months of natural exposure (outdoors, unsheltered or sheltered) in north-west London. The curing regimes were chosen to represent the range of regimes applied on construction sites and involved stripping formwork at day 1 and then:

- no additional curing
- immediate application of a curing membrane
- one day of moist curing (wet hessian sealed in polythene sheet)
- seven days of moist curing (wet hessian sealed in polythene sheet).

Porosity and anhydrous cement content were measured at depths of 0.5 mm, 3.5 mm, 6.5 mm and 20.5 mm into the concrete shortly after curing (at an age of seven days) and again after the nine-month exposure period. This allowed the link between practical curing methods and the microstructure of concrete in the CAZ to be investigated. After nine months of exposure the panels were also tested for abrasion resistance and carbonation depth, to allow the relationship between microstructure in the CAZ and some aspects of durability performance to be investigated. Abrasion resistance and carbonation depth were selected as durability performance measures – not because they are necessarily the mechanisms of greatest concern to concrete structures, but because the first phase of this project highlighted that they are most directly dependent on curing and are also the least complex. Half of the panels have been returned to the exposure site for long-term exposure.

The combination of backscattered electron imaging of polished surfaces in the SEM and greyscale image analysis was confirmed to be a useful method for assessing the effects of curing, being able to quantify microstructural gradients in coarse porosity and anhydrous cement content in the cement paste fraction of concrete. The technique only identifies the larger capillary pores (say > 0.5 µm) and does not have the resolution to pick up the finer capillary pores, nor any of the gel pores. Consequently the porosity determined by the technique represents only a small fraction of the total porosity present. In seven-day old OPC concretes, around 42 per cent of the theoretical capillary porosity (calculated based on the measured degree of hydration and free water/cement ratio using the method described in Neville, 1995) was resolved at a free water/cement ratio of 0.70, reducing to around 23 per cent at a free water/cement ratio of 0.55. However, it is the coarser capillary pores that have the major influence on durability.

It was found that at early ages (eg seven days) curing regime can have a significant effect on the pore structure of concrete very near to the cured surface; poor curing results in higher porosity paste near the surface in relation to the bulk concrete.

An unexpected finding was that differences in curing that resulted in porosity profiles had very little effect on anhydrous cement content. A possible explanation is that the ambient humidity (around 70–80 per cent relative humidity, see Appendix A1) experienced by panels provided with no additional curing after one day in formwork was sufficient to empty larger capillary pores some distance from cement grains, but not the finer capillary pores closer to the cement grains. Consequently hydration continued, but near the concrete surface the resulting hydration products were formed away from the larger capillary pores detected in the SEM.

Microstructural benefits gained from curing were found to diminish with long-term exposure, with the effects of nine months of UK exposure (outdoors unsheltered or sheltered) having a greater influence on microstructure than initial curing. This resulted from both further hydration of the cement and carbonation of the concrete and made it impossible to identify a CAZ depth by nine months.

Exposure environment (sheltered or unsheltered) also had more effect on carbonation depth than initial curing. Nevertheless, both abrasion resistance (Chapter 3) and carbonation depth (Chapter 4) were confirmed as being dependent on curing and correlated well with porosity measured by SEM (at nine months) in the zone affected (surface few millimetres). Lower porosity was associated with increased abrasion resistance (Figure 6.2) and reduced carbonation depth (Figure 6.5). The correlations were good, despite being based on four different concretes. No correlation was observed between abrasion resistance or carbonation depth and anhydrous cement content when the data from the four concretes tested were considered together. However, when each concrete was viewed on its own, the expected trend of increasing abrasion resistance and reducing carbonation depth with reducing anhydrous cement content was usually apparent.

Recommendations are made for further research. These fall into two categories:

- those related to test method development
- those concerned with quantifying the effects of curing on concrete microstructure/ durability.

This latter group is ultimately aimed at establishing the most efficient way of producing durable concrete on site, with particular attention to curing. It would allow guidelines to be established for design/construction which could include "trade-offs" between binder type, water/cement ratio, curing regime and cover depth for different exposure environments. It will enable cover rules and standards to be revised on the basis of improved knowledge and understanding.

Thus six conclusions are drawn.

1. Backscattered electron imaging of polished surfaces in the SEM combined with greyscale image analysis is a useful method for assessing the effects of curing.

2. At early ages (eg seven days) curing regime can have a significant effect on the pore structure of concrete very near to the cured surface; poor curing results in higher porosity paste near the surface in relation to the bulk concrete.

3. Microstructural benefits gained from curing diminish with exposure, with the effects of nine months of UK exposure (outdoors unsheltered or sheltered) having a greater influence on microstructure than curing, such that the full extent of the CAZ could not be identified by nine months.

4. Both abrasion resistance and carbonation depth were dependent on curing and correlated well with porosity measured by SEM (at nine months) in the zone affected, ie in the surface few millimetres. Lower porosity was associated with increased abrasion resistance and reduced carbonation depth.

5. The results confirm the importance of curing surfaces likely to be exposed to abrasion early in their lives.

6. Further work is required to establish guidelines concerning the most efficient way of producing durable concrete on site, taking account of "trade-offs" between choice of curing regime and selection of binder type, water/cement ratio and cover depth depending on the exposure environment.

Contents

LIST OF FIGURES

LIST OF TABLES

ABBREVIATIONS

BSE   Backscattered electron

CAZ   Curing affected zone

CSH   Calcium silicate hydrate

GGBS   Ground granulated blastfurnace slag

OPC   Ordinary Portland cement

PFA   Pulverised fuel ash

SEM   Scanning electron microscope/microscopy

s   Sheltered

u   Unsheltered

1 Introduction

1.1 BACKGROUND

Phase I of the project "The influence of practical on-site curing with special reference to durability and abrasion resistance" reported on a desk review of published information on the subject (CIRIA PR49, Hammersley et al, 1997). The majority of the research had investigated the link between curing conditions and short-term, durability-related performance for several concretes and exposure condition combinations. Whilst often providing good data for the concrete and exposure tested, such data can be difficult to extrapolate to other situations.

In addition to arriving at conclusions on the effects of practical curing (comparable to typical on-site curing) on concrete, in so far as was possible, it was intended that Phase I should identify potentially useful test methods for assessing the effectiveness and extent of on-site curing. Such methods would then be developed further during an essentially laboratory based Phase II programme.

However, in Phase I it was concluded that it was extremely unlikely that any currently available conventional test method could form the basis of assessing on-site curing over the range of environmental exposures envisaged. The Project steering group for this phase concluded that the assessment of curing effectiveness and its influence on durability performance could be most beneficially determined by considering the micro-structure in the curing affected zone (CAZ). This is the zone of concrete near to and including its outer surface, which can be directly affected by active curing measures (CIRIA PR49, *ibid*).

1.2 OBJECTIVES

The objectives of Phase II of the project (covered by this report) were to establish the viability of a method for investigating:

- the link between practical curing methods and the microstructure of concrete in the CAZ
- the relationship between microstructure in the CAZ and durability performance.

This was to take into account practical construction technology and real-life timescales and was intended to help to develop a framework for assessing the relationship between practical curing methods and exposure performance.

1.3 APPROACH

The approach adopted to characterise concrete microstructure was to obtain high magnification images of the concrete using scanning electron microscopy (SEM) and then to use image analysis to covert these into microstructural parameters (essentially porosity and anhydrous cement). Preliminary work was undertaken to develop the SEM method and to demonstrate that differences in microstructural features could be identified and quantified (see Section 5.1.2).

The method was then applied in a large test programme; the main steps are summarised in the flow chart shown in Figure 1.1. Concrete test panels of four different concretes were cured in different ways and were then subjected to natural exposure (outdoors unsheltered or sheltered). After nine months the panels were tested for abrasion resistance and carbonation depth. Abrasion resistance and carbonation depth were selected as durability measures – not because they are necessarily the mechanisms of greatest concern, but because they are known to be dependent on curing. Porosity and anhydrous cement content profiles into the concrete were measured, both shortly after curing (at an age of seven days) and after the nine-month exposure period. Concretes, curing regimes and the corresponding tests are summarised in Table 1.1.

Table 1.1   *Combinations of variables to be examined*

Concrete	Grade	Curing*	Exposure'	SEM at 7 days	Abrasion testing	Carbonation and SEM at 9 months
A		1	u		✓	✓
		2	u			✓
		3	u			✓
OPC	35	4	u		✓	✓
		1	s	✓	✓	✓
		2	s	✓	✓	✓
		3	s	✓	✓	✓
		4	s	✓	✓	
B		1	u			✓
	20	4	u			✓
OPC		1	s	✓	✓	✓
		4	s	✓	✓	✓
C		1	u			✓
	35	4	u			✓
25% PFA		1	s	✓	✓	✓
		4	s	✓	✓	✓
D		1	u			✓
	35	4	u			✓
65% GGBS		1	s	✓	✓	✓
		4	s	✓	✓	✓

* Curing regime: 1 = no additional curing
2 = immediate application of a curing membrane
3 = 1 day moist curing (wet hessian sealed in polythene sheet)
4 = 7 days moist curing (wet hessian sealed in polythene sheet)

' Exposure: u = unsheltered
s = sheltered

It can be seen that 20 combinations of variables are involved, allowing the effects of three cement types, two concrete grades, four curing regimes and two exposure environments to be assessed. Half of the panels (the outdoors unsheltered panels) have been returned to the exposure site for long-term exposure and may be used in future research.

The project was undertaken by Imperial College, who carried out all of the SEM work, with Taywood Engineering Ltd. (TEL) as subcontractors responsible for mix development, panel manufacture, curing, exposure and abrasion and carbonation depth testing.

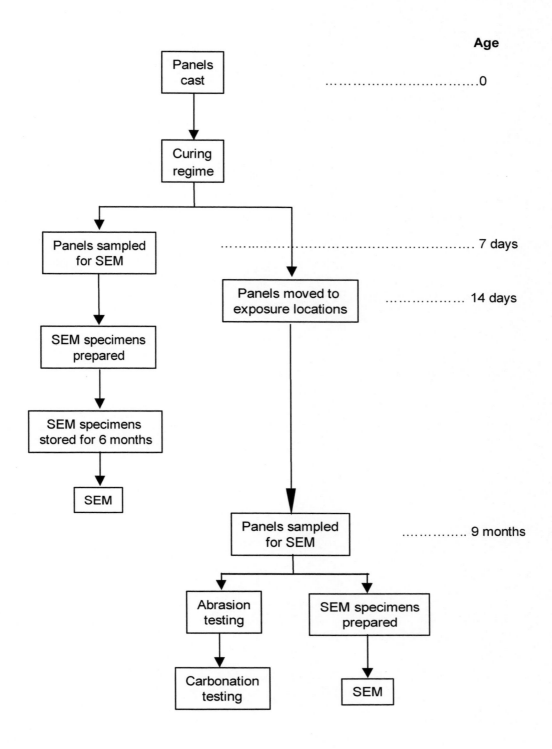

Figure 1.1   *Flow chart showing main activities of test programme*

2 Panels

2.1 CONCRETES

Ideally a wide range of concretes would have been tested, but this had to be tempered by the possible scope of this exploratory project. Four concretes were chosen to cover a range of typical concretes. A trial mix programme by TEL resulted in the four concrete mixes detailed in Table 2.1. In all cases dolerite coarse aggregate and silica sand were used. These aggregates were chosen because they have low and consistent (from particle to particle) water absorption and because preliminary trials showed that they could be readily isolated from the other concrete constituents in the SEM. Table 2.1 also includes three, seven and 28 days compressive strength results for the concrete mixes, based on testing 100 mm cubes to BS 1881 (BSI, 1983).

Table 2.1   *Concrete mix and panel details*

	Concrete A C35–OPC				Concrete B C20–OPC		Concrete C C35–25% PFA		Concrete D C35–65% GGBS	
SSD mix proportions (kg/m^3)										
OPC (BCI, Northfleet)	330				275		281		140	
PFA (Ash Resources, W Burton)	–				–		94		–	
GGBS (Civil & Marine)	–				–		–		260	
20 mm Dolerite (RMC, Cragmill)	818				832		845		805	
10 mm Dolerite (RMC, Cragmill)	409				416		425		400	
Sand (Tilcon, Sevenoaks)	752				765		340		330	
Sand (Redland, Radlett)	–				–		345		340	
Water	181.5				192		169		188	
Water/cement ratio	0.55				0.70		0.45		0.47	
Panel reference	1290	1283	1315	1322	1393	1400	1478	1485	1463	1470
Date of casting	20.10.97		22.10.97		29.10.97		05.11.97		05.11.97	
Slump (mm)	85	80	90	85	170c	175c	130	110	125	140
Mix temperature (°C)	22.3	21.1	16.3	16.9	15.3	15.9	18.6	18.4	17.1	17.7
Curing regime	1+4	1+4	2+3	2+3	1+4	1+4	1+4	1+4	1+4	1+4
Exposure environment	s	u	s	u	s	u	s	u	s	u
Cube strength (MPa)										
3 days	29.5	29.0	28.5	28.0	14.5	14.5	24.5	25.0	18.0	16.0
7 days	37.0	39.0	36.5	38.5	23.5	23.5	33.0	34.5	31.5	29.5
28 days	49.5	49.5	50.5	48.5	31.5	31.5	51.0	51.0	51.5	48.0

2.2 PANEL DETAILS

Four panels from Concrete A and two panels from each of Concretes B, C and D (ie ten panels in total) were cast between 20.10.97 and 5.11.97 at the TEL labs in Southall. Panels were 1 m long × 0.5 m high × 0.15 m thick, cast in plywood formwork, treated with two coats of polyurethane varnish and a minimal amount of mould oil. Each panel was made from a single batch of concrete. Figure 2.1 shows a panel shortly after casting. The exposed upper surface was then sealed with polythene sheeting.

Figure 2.1   *Test panel in formwork*

2.3 CURING

24 hours after casting, the panels were transferred to a large hangar (indoors, but with no temperature control), the formwork was removed and each large face (1 m × 0.5 m) was subjected to one of the following curing regimes, as indicated in Table 1.1:

- no additional curing
- immediate application of a curing membrane (DARAKOTE 90, WR Grace)
- one-day moist curing (wet hessian sealed in polythene sheet)
- seven-day moist curing (wet hessian sealed in polythene sheet).

These curing regimes were chosen to represent the range of regimes commonly applied on site. In the case of the seven-day wet hessian curing regime, the polythene was loosened and the hessian was checked on several occasions to ensure that it was still damp; it was not found necessary to rewet the hessian.

2.4 SEVEN-DAY SAMPLING

At an age of seven days, a top corner (approximately 200 mm wide × 225 mm deep) of one of each pair of panels (ie five panels and ten concrete/curing regime combinations) was removed by drilling 12 mm diameter pilot holes, then using a hammer and chisel. This method of extracting a sample was used to minimise the time of its contact with water used during drilling. The samples were dispatched to Imperial College (IC) and used to prepare specimens for SEM examination (see Section 5.1.3). Figure 2.2 shows the panels after sampling. The fractured surfaces and four edges of the panels were coated with an epoxy-based coating (SIKAFLOOR 67, two-part water thinnable epoxy-based protective coating – three coats for unsheltered panels and two coats for sheltered panels) to minimise biaxial drying, wetting and carbonation during exposure.

2.5 EXPOSURE

All of the panels were left exposed in the hangar until an age of 14 days, to reduce the variation in early exposure environment experienced by panels cast at different times. At 14 days, one of each pair of panels was transferred to an adjacent outdoor, unsheltered location where they were exposed with the faces of interest vertical, approximately parallel to one another and 300 mm apart (as shown in Figure 2.3). This arrangement probably led to different degrees of wetting during rainfall, although examination of the panels after a period of heavy rainfall did not indicate a specific pattern to the wetting.

Figure 2.2   *Sheltered exposure of panels*

Figure 2.3   *Unsheltered exposure of panels*

The other half of the panels (those sampled at seven days for SEM) were left sheltered in the hangar. The temperature and relative humidity (RH) in the hangar, and the temperature and rainfall for the unsheltered exposure panels, were monitored for the nine-month exposure period. The results are presented as graphs in Appendix A1. The probe used to monitor the hangar RH was regularly checked/calibrated at 50 per cent and 80 per cent RH, but cannot be relied upon at RH values above 92 per cent. Recorded measurements of more than 90 per cent in Figure A1.2 are not precise and should only be regarded as indicating that the RH was somewhere above 90 per cent. RH was not monitored adjacent to the unsheltered exposure panels, but RH data for the period of interest from the Meteorological Office weather station at Northolt (around 2 miles north-west of the exposure site in Southall, north-west London) is included as Figure A1.5. The temperature and RH data up to the age of 14 days in the hangar are of particular interest and are included as Table A1.1.

2.6 NINE-MONTH SAMPLING

At an age of nine months, a top corner (approximately 200 mm wide × 225 mm deep) of each panel (ie ten panels and all 20 concrete/curing regime combinations) was removed by drilling 12 mm diameter pilot holes, then using a hammer and chisel. This sample was delivered to Imperial College (IC) and used to prepare specimens for SEM (see Section 5.1.3). Some of the panels were tested for abrasion resistance (Section 3) and all of the panels were tested for carbonation depth (Section 4). The unsheltered panels were then returned to their exposure site for further exposure. The abrasion resistance testing was carried out primarily on the sheltered panels; because of the destructive nature of the abrasion resistance test there was insufficient undamaged surface remaining on these panels to warrant their continued exposure.

3 Abrasion resistance

3.1 METHOD

After nine months of exposure, 12 of the 20 cured surfaces were tested for abrasion resistance. Abrasion resistance was measured using the Standard Rolling Wheels test, originally developed by the Cement and Concrete Association and now a widely accepted measure of abrasion resistance (Sadegzadeh and Kettle, 1988). The abrasion resistance is expressed in terms of the depth of wear produced after a 15-minute exposure period. Three tests were undertaken on each of the cured surfaces, as shown in Figure 3.1.

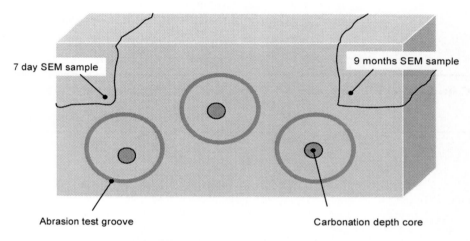

Figure 3.1   *Location of tests on a panel surface*

3.2 RESULTS

The individual and average results are presented in Table 3.1 overleaf.

3.3 DISCUSSION

Generally the results are as might be expected, with longer curing and unsheltered exposure (allowing further hydration of the concrete surface) improving abrasion resistance. Concrete grade is confirmed as being important and, for the same grade, the plain OPC concrete was more resistant than the PFA concrete which was more resistant than the GGBS concrete. Average results range from 0.38 mm for Concrete A, subjected to the most thorough curing (Regime 4) and then externally exposed, to 1.46 mm for the low grade concrete (Concrete B), subjected to no additional curing after demoulding (Regime 1) and exposed in a sheltered environment. These results are poor compared to the performance expected from concrete floor slabs in medium industrial environments, which have been classified as "good" when the abrasion depth is less than 0.2 mm, "poor" when the abrasion depth is greater than 0.4 mm and "normal" when in between these two values (Kettle and Sadegzaden, 1987).

Concrete A complied with the British Standard minimum grade and cement content limits for such floors (C40 and 325 kg/m^3 respectively) (BSI, 1987), but the performance was verging on "poor", even when well cured. One possible explanation is that the concrete had not been finished by the combination of power floating and power trowelling which is known to give enhanced abrasion resistance (Kettle and Sadegzaden, 1987).

The only result contrary to expectations was that for Concrete A, as one day of moist curing (Regime 3) produced lower abrasion resistance than no additional curing (Regime 1). Although the difference was small – 0.75 mm (A3s) versus 0.64 mm (A1s) – the same trend was observed in both the carbonation (Table 3.1) and SEM (Section 5.3.2) results suggesting that this represents a real difference between the cured surfaces rather than experimental scatter. The effect is probably due to the placing temperature of the concrete (see Table 2.1) in A1 (22.3°C) being 6°C higher than for the concrete in A3 (16.3°C), producing more extensive hydration during the first 24 hours (prior to stripping the formwork) in A1 than produced in the first 48 hours for A3. It should be noted that with the exception of the A1/4 panels, the placing temperature of the concrete in all of the other panels fell within the relatively narrow range of 17.0 ± 1.7°C.

Table 3.1 *Abrasion and carbonation depth test results*

Concrete	Grade	Curing*	Exposure	Abrasion (mm)		Carbonation depth (mm)	
				Individual results	Average	Individual results	Average
		1	u	0.51, 0.58, 0.53	0.54	0.7, 1.1, 0.7	0.8
		2	u			1.3, 1.8, 1.2	1.4
A	35	3	u			1.1, 0.9, 0.7	0.9
		4	u	0.37, 0.42, 0.36	0.38	0.3, 0.8, 0.8	0.6
OPC		1	s	0.66, 0.67, 0.58	0.64	2.0, 1.9, 2.3	2.1
		2	s	0.49, 0.62, 0.56	0.56	3.1, 2.7, 1.8	2.5
		3	s	0.74, 0.82, 0.70	0.75	3.1, 3.0, 2.7	2.9
		4	s	0.44, 0.41, 0.51	0.45	0.7, 1.0, 1.5	1.1
B	20	1	u			4.0, 2.4, 3.8	3.4
		4	u	1.31, 1.61, 1.47	1.46	3.5, 3.8, 3.6	3.6
OPC		1	s	0.98, 1.02, 0.96	0.99	6.0, 4.9, 5.9	5.6
		4	s			5.0, 3.4, 3.8	4.0
C	35	1	u			1.3, 1.4, 1.2	1.3
		4	u	0.80, 0.92, 0.75	0.82	0.6, 2.7, 0.3	1.2
25% PFA		1	s	0.74, 0.89, 0.73	0.79	3.3, 3.2, 2.5	3.0
		4	s			4.0, 4.1, 1.9	3.3
D	35	1	u			2.6, 2.3, 4.7	3.2
		4	u	1.20, 1.22, 1.22	1.21	2.6, 2.2, 1.8	2.2
65% GGBS		1	s	0.92, 1.04, 0.99	0.98	6.1, 5.8, 6.0	6.0
		4	s			3.5, 3.0, 4.3	3.6

* Curing regime: 1 = no additional curing

2 = immediate application of a curing membrane

3 = 1-day moist curing (wet hessian sealed in polythene)

4 = 7-day moist curing (wet hessian sealed in polythene)

4 Carbonation depth

4.1 METHOD

After the abrasion testing had been completed (ie after nine months of exposure), three No. 50 mm diameter cores were removed from each cured surface (ie all 20 mixing/curing combinations). For the 12 surfaces that were abrasion-tested, one core was taken from within each of the three circular abrasion test grooves, as shown in Figure 3.1. The cores were split in half and sprayed with phenolphthalein indicator. Carbonation depth was measured at eight equally spaced increments across the 50 mm wide cores (ie 24 measurements for each cured surface) to the nearest 0.5 mm.

4.2 RESULTS

The average carbonation depth results (average for each core and average of the three cores) for each cured surface are presented to the nearest 0.1 mm in Table 3.1.

4.3 DISCUSSION

The average carbonation depths for each cured surface were 0.6–6.0 mm. In all cases, as expected, unsheltered exposure resulted in less carbonation than sheltered exposure. This is because the rate of carbonation is relatively low at the high moisture contents found for concretes directly exposed to the wet UK climate (Buenfeld, Hassanein and Jones, 1988). Strength grade had the expected effect with lower carbonation depth associated with higher strength (compare Concrete A with Concrete B). As with the abrasion testing, the plain OPC concrete was more resistant than the PFA concrete, which was more resistant than the GGBS concrete. There are eight pairs of results enabling Curing Regimes 1–4 to be compared. Six of the eight pairs indicated reduced carbonation depth due to longer curing.

5   Scanning electron microscopy (SEM)

5.1   METHOD

5.1.1   Brief background to SEM and image analysis

The scanning electron microscope (SEM) is used extensively in materials science and has many applications in concrete petrography. The underlying principle is that a specimen is bombarded with a beam of accelerated electrons which interact with the specimen to produce secondary electrons, backscattered electrons (BSEs) and x-rays. Different detectors are used to collect these signals to provide the information required.

BSE images (used in this project) are formed due to elastic collisions between incident electrons and electrons in the specimen. The scattering of these electrons increases as the atomic number of the material increases, and can therefore reveal difference in composition; thus the higher the mean atomic number of the phase, the higher the intensity of the BSE signal. On this basis, specific phases within the cement paste and concrete can be determined by the relative intensity of the BSE signal. The intensity of backscattering is also affected by topography, therefore flat polished specimens are essential to obtain a compositional image.

The SEM image is formed of lines which are then digitised into pixels, with a greyscale range ranging from white, through the various shades of grey, to black. Grey level thresholds are established and the image then undergoes binarisation, where the pixels become either black or white at a particular threshold level. Each phase can thus be successively identified. If necessary, the image can undergo processing by cycles of erosion and dilation to separate features. The image can then undergo analysis to quantify the phases identified.

Appendix A2 provides a more detailed background to SEM and image analysis.

5.1.2   Method development

Equipment

The SEM used was the JEOL JSM 5410LV linked to an Oxford Instruments ISIS microanalysis system, based in the Concrete Durability Group of the Department of Civil and Environmental Engineering at Imperial College.

Magnification

The resolution of the technique depends on the magnification used. Too low a magnification and the features of interest (larger capillary pores and anhydrous cement particles) are not resolved. Too high a magnification and an impractically large number of fields must be imaged and analysed in order to achieve statistically acceptable results. Preliminary work at different magnifications determined that a magnification of around 500× was optimal for the purposes of this study.

It should be recognised that at this magnification only the larger capillary pores (say >0.5 μm) are resolved and not the finer capillary pores nor any of the gel pores.

Consequently, the porosity determined by the technique represents only a fraction of the total porosity present. Fortunately, it is these coarser capillary pores that have the most influence on durability (see Section 5.3.1). Anhydrous cement particles of less than around 0.5 µm are also unresolved at a magnification of 500×. However, such particles are expected to represent only a very small fraction of the anhydrous cement present. The resolution could be improved by using a higher magnification, but doubling the magnification would require a four-fold increase in the number of fields imaged and analysed in order to represent the same area of cement paste. Time and resources available in this project did not permit the use of higher magnification levels.

SEM and image analyser variables

A BSE image with good compositional contrast is essential for quantitative analysis. This depends on the operating conditions of both the microscope and the image analyser. Thus it was necessary to investigate and define the optimal SEM and image analyser working conditions to be used. Based on the known effects of the SEM and image analyser variables on the image, the key variables (contrast, brightness, beam current, etc) were adjusted to obtain an optimal and constant distribution of greyscale between the various phases of OPC, OPC + PFA and OPC + GGBS concretes.

This resulted in the adoption of the following values for the key variables: 0° stage tilt, 15 mm working distance, 15 nm beam spot size, 1 nA (nominally) probe/beam current (controlled by spot size and filament load current), 20 kV accelerating voltage, 75–80 µA loaded beam current, 9 Pa pressure in the vacuum chamber and a scanning speed of 100 µs dwell per pixel.

BSE images and greyscale distribution

Figure 5.1(a) shows a typical BSE image of Concrete A. Figure 5.1(b) shows the corresponding greyscale distribution, where the values recorded for individual pixels making up an image are ranked on a scale of 0–255 and are plotted against frequency. Five phases are represented: porosity (P), calcium silicate hydrate (CSH) gel with AFt and AFm, aggregate (AGG), calcium hydroxide (CH) and anhydrous cement (AN). The two phases of most interest in this study, porosity and anhydrous cement, are at extreme ends of the spectrum, being the darkest and lightest phases respectively.

The anhydrous cement phase has a fairly narrow grey level, and therefore results in a sharp peak, enabling easy identification – see Figure 5.1(b) and (d).

The samples are impregnated with resin to enable them to be adequately polished (see Section 5.1.3). In practice, the resin does not fill all the pores present. The unimpregnated pores should generate minimal BSEs and appear black, giving a greyscale value of zero in the greyscale histogram. The impregnated pores should not have a high greyscale value due to absorption of electrons by the resin. However, shallow and in-filled pores do generate some backscatter and register a greyscale value. Thus it can be observed that the peak for porosity is not always distinct. Furthermore, the CSH is represented by a rather broad peak due to variations in its composition and incorporated porosity, partially overlapping the porosity range. The differentiation between porosity and CSH in the setting of the greyscale threshold value is operator-dependent and is achieved by selecting an arbitrary point on the lower slope of the peak produced by the CSH, corresponding to a level giving a visually satisfactory cut off. This is illustrated in Figure 5.1(c).

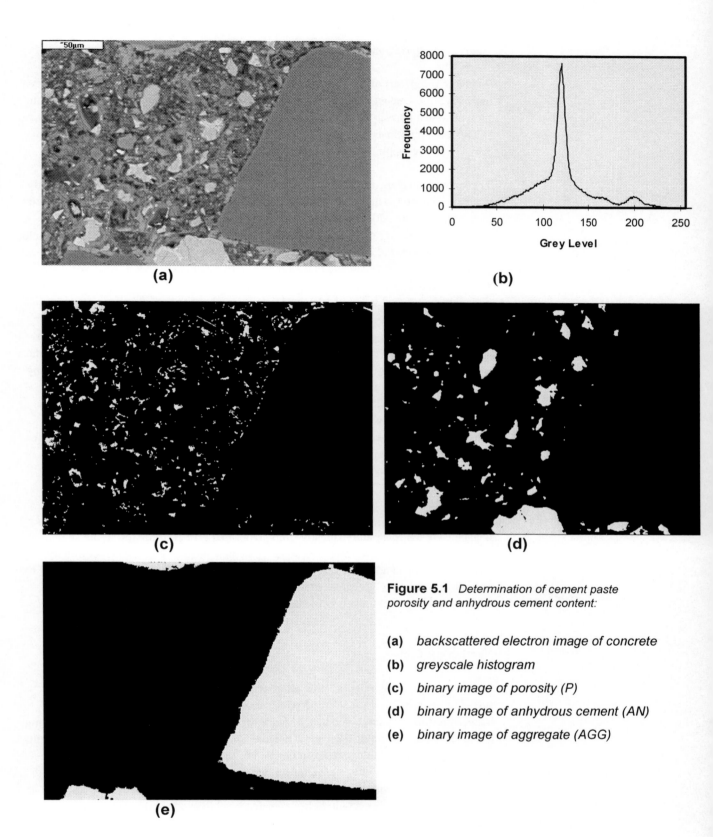

Figure 5.1 *Determination of cement paste porosity and anhydrous cement content:*

(a) *backscattered electron image of concrete*

(b) *greyscale histogram*

(c) *binary image of porosity (P)*

(d) *binary image of anhydrous cement (AN)*

(e) *binary image of aggregate (AGG)*

Aggregate separation

Although the effects of curing are to be characterised in terms of variations in porosity and anhydrous cement content, it is also necessary to define and quantify the aggregate present so that porosity and anhydrous cement content of the cement paste alone may be calculated. Preliminary work showed that commonly used concreting aggregates have grey levels overlapping with the CSH – see Figure 5.1(b).

The method developed to deal with aggregate was as follows. Specimens were initially manually scanned to determine the location of coarse aggregate particles. Images were then acquired automatically along preset lines of around 20 mm length parallel to the cured surface, avoiding fields entirely comprised of coarse aggregate particles. For fields partially comprised of aggregate, the aggregate particles were isolated by using a "gradient technique" (available in the Oxford Instruments ISIS IMQUANT software suite as GRADIENT). This creates an image whose grey level is defined by differentiation of the original image. In the gradient image, sharp variations of greyscale in the original image that normally occur at the edge of a phase are bright and areas with smoother variation in grey level are dark. Although the aggregate and CSH have overlapping greyscales, the aggregate particles are evenly grey (see Figure 5.1(a)) while the CSH is fragmented by pores, calcium hydroxide and small clinker particles of differing greyscale. Hence the gradient image shows complete aggregate grains, but small fragmented areas of CSH. An erosion (even removal of binary pixels from the surface of a particle) technique was applied to clean away the fragments of CSH and then reconstruction (recovery of remaining particles to their original shapes) was applied to recover the aggregate particles to their original forms. The result of this aggregate separation is illustrated in Figure 5.1(e).

Image collection

Images were collected automatically from predefined grid coordinates on the specimen utilised the computer-controlled motorised specimen stage of the SEM. Preliminary work demonstrated adequate stability of the beam current over the acquisition period for beam drift (leading to variations in image greyscale thresholds due to changes in contrast and brightness level) not to have a significant effect on the results, once the SEM had "warmed up".

Numbers of fields

Linked to the optimal magnification issue, discussed above, is the need to analyse sufficient fields to produce a statistically acceptable result. There was a fine balance between testing very large numbers of fields for a small number of specimens or testing a smaller number of fields for a wider range of specimens/variables. Figure 5.2 presents the average porosity of the paste as a function of the number of fields included in the analysis for four depth increments, for A1 and A4 respectively. This shows how accuracy increases with the number of fields included in the analysis. In the results that follow (see Section 5.2), 28–40 fields were averaged to produce the values of porosity and anhydrous cement content reported for each depth.

Depths for analysis

Preliminary work suggested that the CAZ would be less than 10 mm. Depths for analysis were chosen as 0.5 mm, 3.5 mm, 6.5 mm and 20.5mm, the latter depth representing bulk concrete expected to be outside of the CAZ.

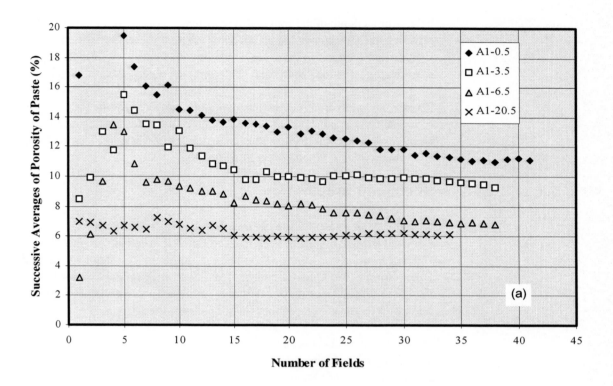

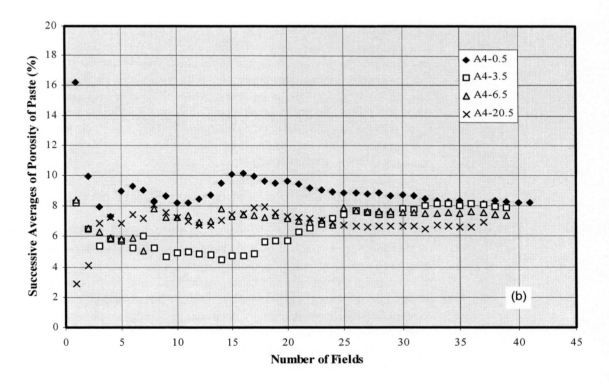

Figure 5.2   *Successive averages of porosity vs. number of fields:*
(a) A1, seven days, (b) A4, seven days.

At a magnification of 500×, each field (such as that shown in Figure 5.1(a)) represents an area of around 270 μm wide × 200 μm deep and so, for example, samples reported as being from a depth of 3.5 mm really represent 3.4–3.6 mm. In a small number of cases, insufficient fields containing an adequate amount of cement paste could be produced by a single line scan and in these cases two lines of fields were imaged, therefore representing a 0.4 mm-wide band centred on the reported depth.

Porosity and anhydrous cement profiles were measured for the ten mix/curing combinations (as indicated in Table 1.1) seven days after casting, and for all 20 mix/curing/exposure combinations after nine months of exposure. This involved taking and analysing a total of around 4000 SEM images.

5.1.3 Specimen preparation

45 mm × 22 mm (depth from the cured surface) × 6 mm specimens were cut from the extracted corners of panels, such that the concrete specimen originated from at least 150 mm from the top of a panel, at least 75 mm from the side of a panel and at least 25 mm from a drill hole. Calcium hydroxide-saturated water was used as the cutting fluid to minimise leaching of calcium hydroxide. These specimens were then surface-dried with tissue and placed in a small incubator for drying.

The longest period between the first pilot hole being drilled and the specimen being placed in the incubator was 2.5 hours for the seven-day tests and 72 hours for the nine-month tests. In all cases, the longest period between a specimen being wetted during cutting and being placed in the incubator was 45 minutes.

The incubators were maintained at $21 \pm 1°C$, 55 ± 4 per cent RH and near zero CO_2. This drying regime was adopted to remove capillary water rapidly, without causing unnatural microstructural damage. The specimens were removed after 28 days in an incubator and were vacuum-impregnated with resin within ten minutes. The resin was hardened at 50°C for eight hours. The impregnated specimens were lapped on 120 μm sand cloth for 30 minutes and were then polished on a polishing machine at grades of 6 μm, 3 μm, 1 μm and finally 0.25 μm diamond. This process did not involve any further contact with water. Before and after SEM, specimens were stored in the same incubators, wrapped in polythene.

5.1.4 Effect of SEM sample storage conditions on results

The seven-day specimens were stored as described in Section 5.1.3 for around six months and were then tested over the two-month period, prior to the nine-month specimens becoming available. In this way the SEM work was continuous and undertaken by a single operator, reducing the likelihood of operator-induced variations between the seven-day and nine-month results. Concern was expressed that the seven-day polished block specimens may have changed during storage prior to testing. The specimen preparation method and specimen storage conditions were designed to eliminate this risk. Two mechanisms that could induce a change are further hydration and carbonation. The samples were resin-impregnated and were then stored in polythene bags inside an incubator at 55 per cent RH (ie far lower than that necessary for hydration) and near zero CO_2 (minimising the risk of carbonation) until testing.

Samples examined showed no signs of further hydration which would result in hydration products forming on the polished surface, nor of carbonation which results in a darkening of BSE SEM images.

As a further check, a new set of specimens were prepared and tested at seven days and after six months of storage. Cement paste specimens were used to allow any subtle effects to be identified that might be masked if aggregate was present. 0.55 water/cement was used to be comparable with Concrete A. Specimens were cured in sealed containers and the internal cement paste (avoiding edge effects) was used as the basis of the comparison. The porosity (percentage) was 7.07 ± 0.58 (standard error) after seven days and 6.71 ± 0.94 after six months. The anhydrous cement content (percentage) was 9.38 ± 0.79 after seven days and 8.82 ± 0.66 after six months. In both cases, the difference between seven days and six months is small in relation to the standard errors, giving further confidence in the storage method.

5.2 RESULTS

The porosity and anhydrous cement content profiles for seven-day specimens of Concretes A–D are presented in Figures 5.3–5.6 respectively. The equivalent results for the nine-month old specimens of Concretes A–D are presented in Figures 5.7–5.10 respectively. All of the graphs are plotted to the same scale to allow easy comparison. As described above, each point on the graph is the result of the analysis of at least 30 separate fields. The error bars shown for each point represent ± 1 standard error.

Figure 5.11 is a histogram showing the influence of concrete type, curing regime and exposure regime on porosity at 0.5 mm depth. Figures 5.12–5.14 are equivalent, but for depths of 3.5mm, 6.5 mm and 20.5 mm respectively. Figure 5.15 is a histogram showing the influence of concrete type, curing regime and exposure regime on anhydrous cement content at 0.5 mm depth. Figures 5.16–5.18 are equivalent, but for depths of 3.5mm, 6.5 mm and 20.5 mm respectively.

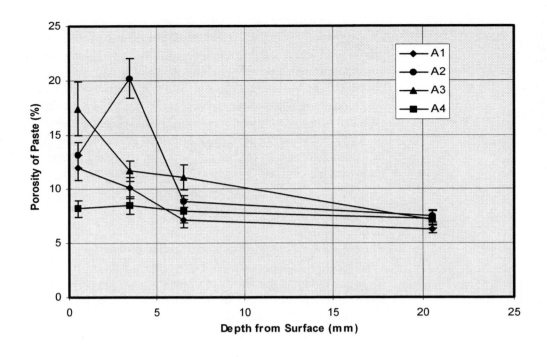

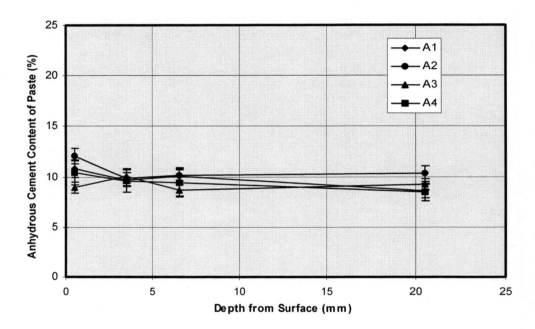

Figure 5.3   *Porosity and anhydrous cement content of cement paste vs. depth for seven-day old Concrete A specimens*

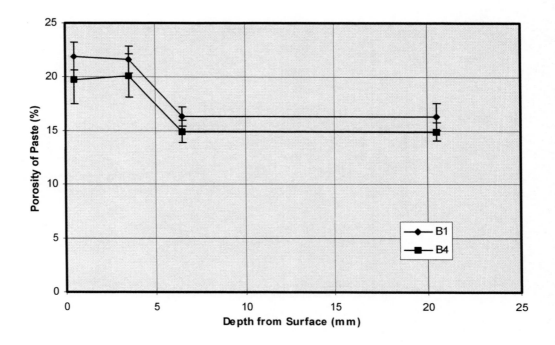

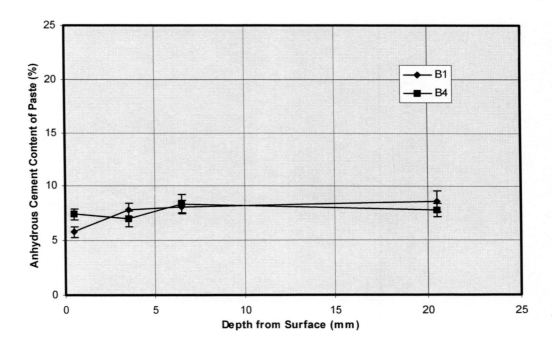

Figure 5.4   *Porosity and anhydrous cement content of cement paste vs. depth for seven-day old Concrete B specimens*

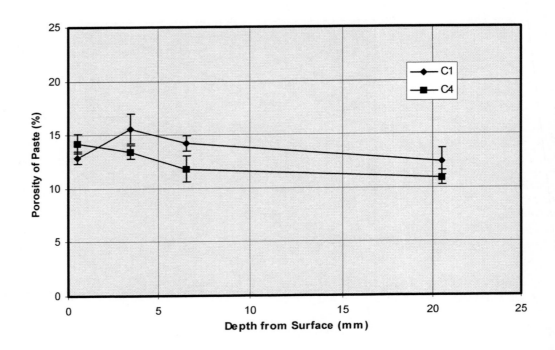

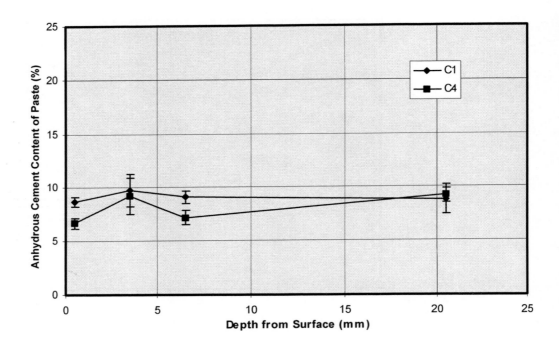

Figure 5.5   *Porosity and anhydrous cement content of cement paste vs. depth for seven-day old Concrete C specimens*

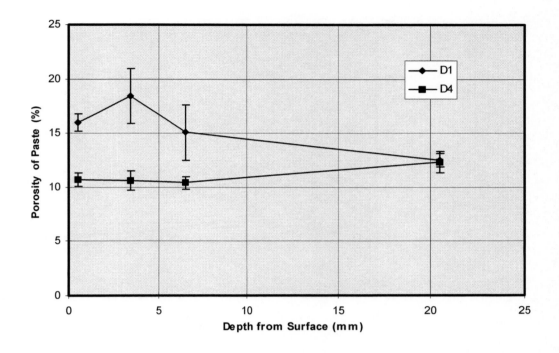

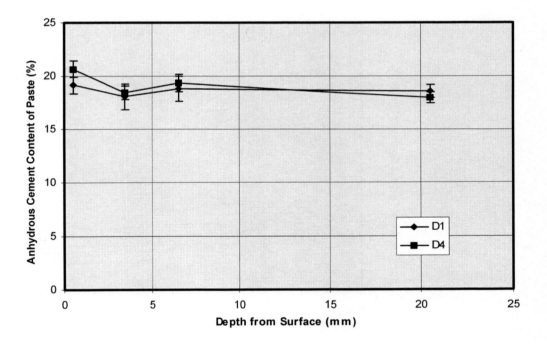

Figure 5.6   *Porosity and anhydrous cement content of cement paste vs. depth for seven-day old Concrete D specimens*

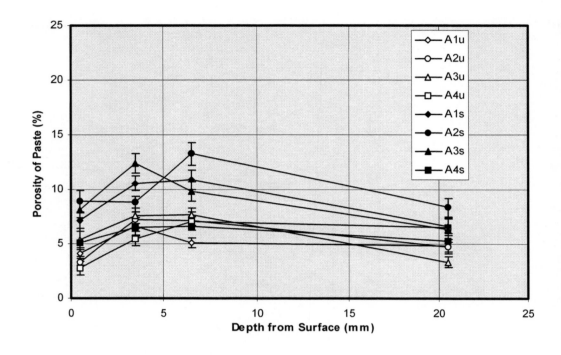

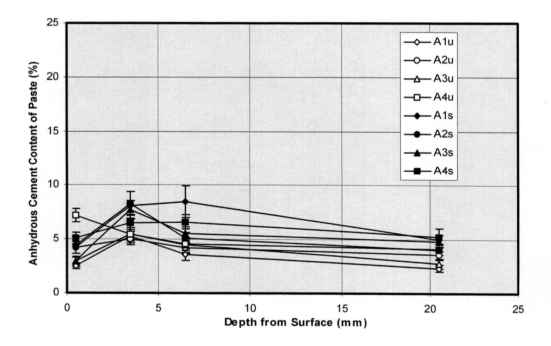

Figure 5.7 *Porosity and anhydrous cement content of cement paste vs. depth for nine-month old Concrete A specimens*

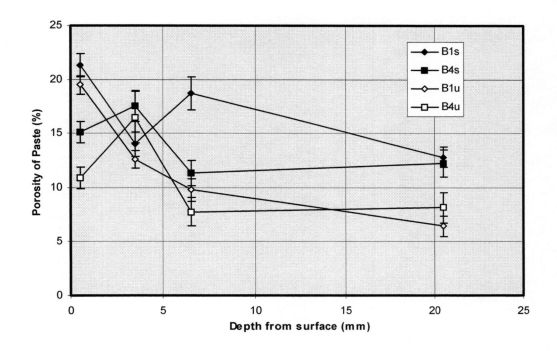

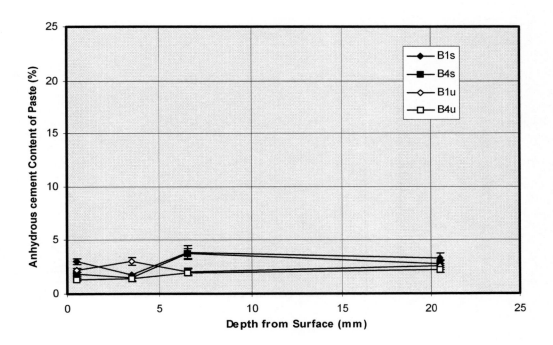

Figure 5.8   *Porosity and anhydrous cement content of cement paste vs. depth for nine-month old Concrete B specimens*

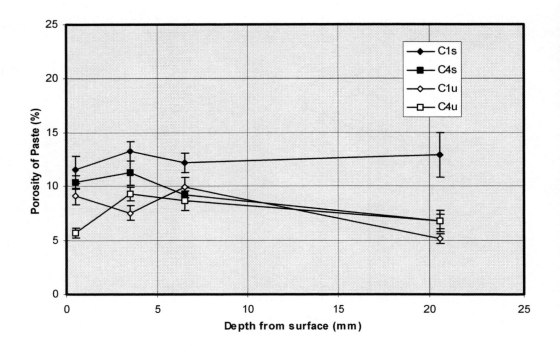

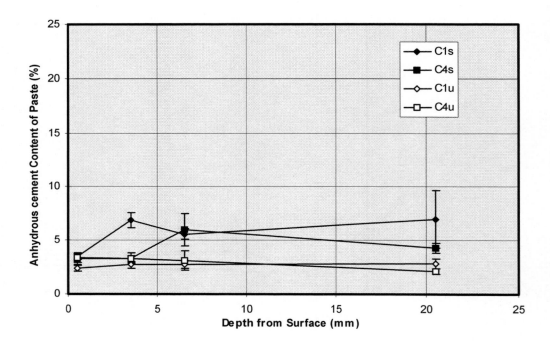

Figure 5.9   *Porosity and anhydrous cement content of cement paste vs. depth for nine-month old Concrete C specimens*

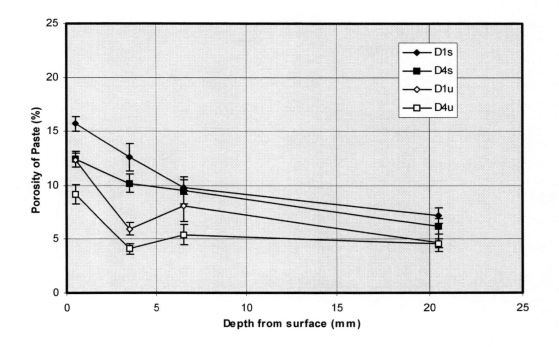

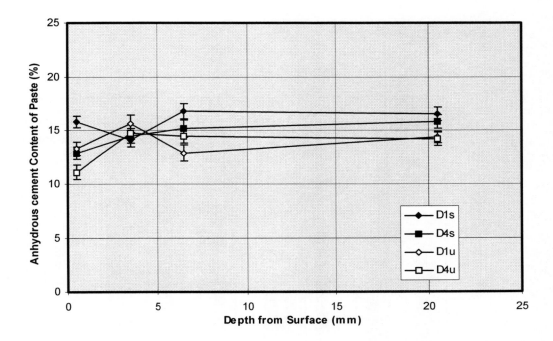

Figure 5.10 *Porosity and anhydrous cement content of cement paste vs. depth for nine-month old Concrete D specimens*

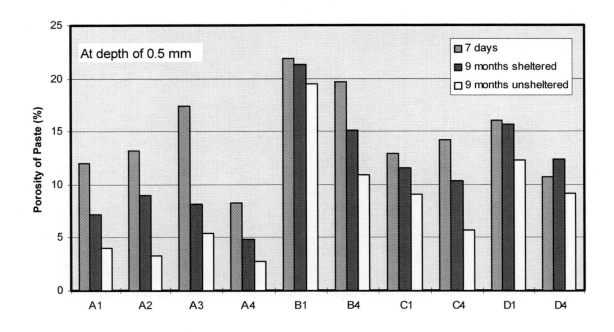

Figure 5.11 *Porosity of the cement paste at 0.5 mm depth as a function of concrete type, curing regime and exposure history*

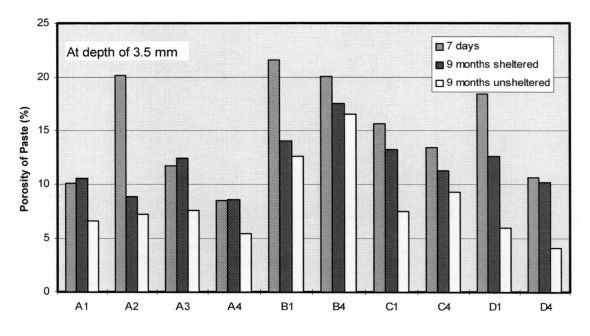

Figure 5.12 *Porosity of the cement paste at 3.5 mm depth as a function of concrete type, curing regime and exposure history*

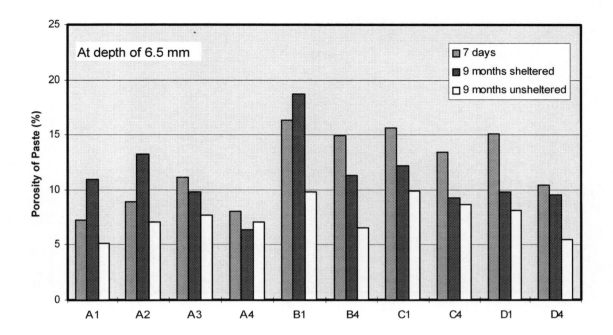

Figure 5.13 *Porosity of the cement paste at 6.5 mm depth as a function of concrete type, curing regime and exposure history*

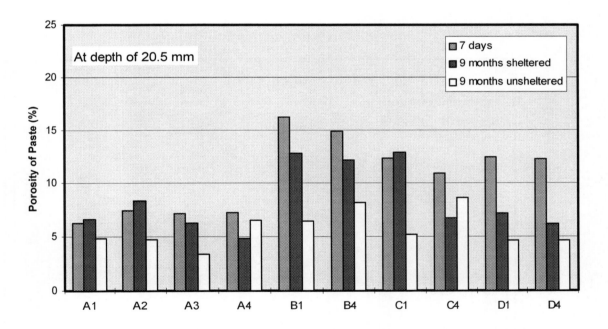

Figure 5.14 *Porosity of the cement paste at 20.5 mm depth as a function of concrete type, curing regime and exposure history*

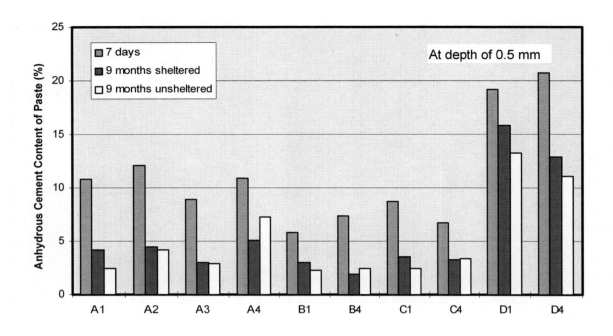

Figure 5.15   *Anhydrous cement content of the cement paste at 0.5 mm depth as a function of concrete type, curing regime and exposure history*

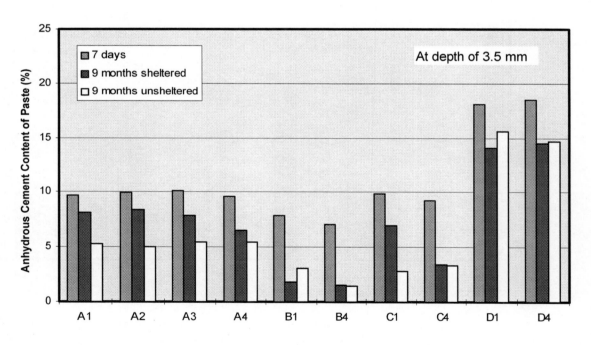

Figure 5.16   *Anhydrous cement content of the cement paste at 3.5 mm depth as a function of concrete type, curing regime and exposure history*

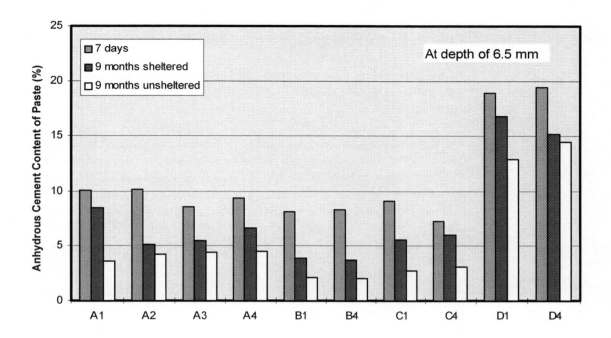

Figure 5.17   *Anhydrous cement content of the cement paste at 6.5 mm depth as a function of concrete type, curing regime and exposure history*

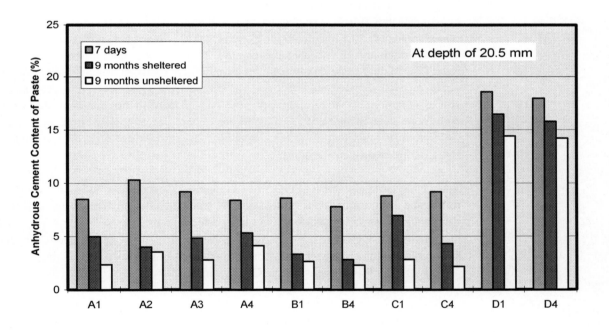

Figure 5.18   *Anhydrous cement content of the cement paste at 20.5 mm depth as a function of concrete type, curing regime and exposure history*

5.3   DISCUSSION

5.3.1   Effect of concrete type on bulk results

First, effects unlikely to be associated with curing regime (or the exposure regime) were addressed by considering the seven-day results at the greatest depth examined (20.5 mm).

The degree of hydration can be estimated by dividing the measured anhydrous cement content by the original (before any hydration) volumetric cement content of the paste (the latter calculated based on the specific gravity of the cement and the free water/cement ratio). Using this approach, the average anhydrous cement content at 20.5 mm depth for Concrete A (see Figure 5.3) represents a degree of hydration of around 77 per cent at seven days. This degree of hydration for 0.55 free water/cement ratio paste should result in a capillary porosity of around 31 per cent (for calculation method see Neville, 1995).

It can be seen that the measured porosity was only around 7 per cent, confirming that only a relatively small fraction (23 per cent) of the capillary porosity is large enough to be resolved by the SEM. However, these larger capillary pores are likely to be the most important pores from the durability viewpoint, because most deterioration processes are controlled by transport (Buenfeld, 1997) and it is the larger pores that contribute most to transport in concrete (Garboczi, 1995).

Comparing Concretes A and B (see Figure 5.14), the result of the higher water/cement ratio of Concrete B is as expected, paste of higher porosity. The average anhydrous cement content at 20.5 mm depth for Concrete B (see Figure 5.4) indicates a degree of hydration of around 75 per cent at seven days. This degree of hydration for 0.70 free water/cement ratio paste should result in a capillary porosity of around 42 per cent. It can be seen that the measured porosity was around 15 or 16 per cent, representing around 37 per cent of the capillary porosity. This increase in the fraction of the capillary porosity resolved in the SEM (37 per cent for Concrete B as opposed to 23 per cent for Concrete A) is consistent with the expectation that capillary pores are on average larger at higher free water/cement ratios.

When considering the effect of GGBS by comparing Concretes A and D, it should be recognised that the anhydrous cement content value includes any anhydrous GGBS as well as OPC. Not much GGBS would be expected to hydrate by seven days, particularly in a relatively thin element not experiencing a significant early age temperature cycle. This is reflected in the higher anhydrous cement content (Figure 5.18) and higher porosity (Figure 5.14) figures for the GGBS concrete.

Considering the effect of PFA by comparing Concretes A and C, part (but not all) of the anhydrous PFA overlapped the anhydrous OPC greyscale and so the anhydrous cement content reported includes all of the anhydrous OPC and some of the anhydrous PFA. Consequently, although the porosity of the PFA concrete is higher than that of the OPC concrete (Figure 5.14), which is expected at seven days, the anhydrous cement content measured (Figure 5.18) turns out to be about the same.

5.3.2 Effect of curing on seven-day results

Figures 5.3–5.6 show the effect of curing on the seven-day profiles. In general, the anhydrous cement content varies very little with depth, with any effect of curing regime being slight. Variations in porosity with depth and curing are more complex. Generally poor curing (Regime 1) results in higher porosity near to the surface in relation to the bulk concrete (20.5 mm depth), while seven days of moist curing (Regime 4) leads to far less variation with depth.

Considering in detail Concrete A (Figure 5.3), it can be seen that at 0.5 mm depth, seven days of moist curing (A4) resulted in the measured porosity being around 8 per cent, as opposed to around 12 per cent for no moist curing (A1); the error bars indicate that the difference is very significant. There also appears to be a significant difference for these concretes at the 3.5 mm depth increment, but by a depth of 6.5 mm there seems to be little significant difference between the two curing regimes. The measured anhydrous cement profiles for A1 and A4 show no significant difference in anhydrous cement content at any of the depths tested. This is rather surprising in the case of 0.5 mm depth, bearing in mind that moist curing reduced the porosity at this depth, presumably by allowing more extensive hydration. A possible explanation is that the ambient humidity (around 70–80 per cent RH; see Appendix A1) that Curing Regime 1 involved after demoulding was sufficient to empty larger capillary pores some distance from cement grains, but not the finer capillary pores closer to the cement grains. Consequently hydration continued for A1, but near the concrete surface the resulting hydration products were formed away from the larger capillary pores detected in the SEM.

The concretes subjected to membrane curing (A2) and one day of moist curing (A3) had higher porosity in the first three depth increments (ie in the surface 7 mm) than the uncured concrete (A1). This is consistent with A1 having lower carbonation depth than A2 or A3 and lower abrasion depth than A3 (see Table 3.1) after nine months. As discussed earlier (see Section 3.3) this seems to represent a real difference between the cured surfaces rather than experimental scatter and is probably due to the placing temperature of the concrete in A1 (22.3°C) being 6°C higher than for the concrete in A3 (16.3°C), producing more extensive hydration during the first 24 hours (prior to stripping the formwork) in A1 than produced in the first 48 hours for A3.

The porosity measured for A2 at 3.5 mm appears to be anomalously high. Re-examining the SEM specimen showed that the area available for testing was limited by it having a disproportionately high aggregate content at this depth. As a consequence it was not possible to sample new (ie not included in the earlier testing) fields to independently check the original value, but reanalysing the images from the originally examined fields gave the original result.

Concrete B (Figure 5.4) showed higher porosity in the surface two depth increments than in the bulk concrete regardless of curing regime. The effect is substantial (around a 30 per cent increase) and may be the result of segregation/bleeding of this rather lean mix producing cement paste of higher water/cement ratio at the surface than in the bulk.

Of the four concretes tested, the effect of poor curing is most marked for the GGBS concrete (Concrete D, Figure 5.6), where poor curing resulted in an increase in porosity in the first three depth increments of around 50 per cent. There was no significant difference in porosity at 20.5 mm depth, nor between anhydrous cement contents measured at any of the four depths.

The depths for analysis (0.5 mm, 3.5 mm, 6.5 mm and 20.5 mm) were not chosen with a view to defining the depth of CAZs, but the results shed some light on the subject. Figures 5.3–5.6 indicate CAZ depths of 3.5–6.5 mm for Concrete A and 6.5–20.5 mm for Concretes C and D. More porosity measurements at different depths on the same SEM specimens would allow CAZ depths to be defined more accurately (see recommendations in Section 8).

5.3.3 Effect of exposure on nine-month results

Exposure history is found to have a major effect on the results and this needs to be considered in order to isolate effects attributable to curing alone. Consequently, exposure (this section) is dealt with before curing (next section).

In every case (ten concrete mix/curing regime combinations × four depth increments = 40 cases) both the porosity and the anhydrous cement content of the unsheltered exposed concrete were lower at nine months than measured at seven days. This trend was expected and is due to the continued hydration of the cement. Even the cement in the 0.5 mm depth increment was able to continue to hydrate because of the regular rainfall and high humidity of the unsheltered UK environment (see meteorological data in Appendix A1).

In every case (ie 40/40) the anhydrous cement content of the sheltered concrete was also lower at nine months than the value measured at seven days. This shows that there was continued hydration even at 0.5 mm depth, despite the concrete not being exposed to liquid water. Reference to Figure A1.2 shows that the concrete spent long periods at a relative humidity of greater than 90 per cent; this would have supported further hydration (CIRIA PR49, Hammersley et al, 1997).

Some values of porosity and anhydrous cement content did not follow the general trends. The exceptions are shown in Table 5.1, which is based on analysis of Figures 5.11–5.18. For example: u < s at an age of nine months – the porosity of unsheltered concrete was expected to be lower than that subjected to sheltered exposure. This was the case for all samples at depths of 0–1 mm and 3–4 mm, but at 6–7 mm the reverse was the case for sample A4. It can be seen that there were ten exceptions (out of 40 cases) overall: one exception at 0.5 mm depth, and three exceptions at each of 3.5 mm, 6.5 mm and 20.5 mm depth. Five of the exceptions were marginal and are shown in brackets.

In 37 out of 40 cases the porosity of the unsheltered concrete was lower than that of the equivalent sheltered concrete and in 34 out of 40 cases the anhydrous cement content of the unsheltered concrete was also lower than that of the equivalent sheltered concrete. This shows that although the sheltered concrete continued to hydrate, generally it did not do so to the same extent as the unsheltered concrete.

For Concrete A, the most striking change between seven days and nine months is the change in shape of both the porosity and anhydrous cement content profiles. Whereas at seven days the porosity of the concretes that were not kept moist was higher in the surface few millimetres than at greater depth (eg Figure 5.3), at nine months this trend was reversed (eg Figure 5.7). At nine months the porosity and anhydrous cement contents were lower in the surface increment (0.5 mm) and the deepest increment (20.5 mm) than in the intermediate increments (3.5 mm and 6.5 mm), resulting in "concave-down" profiles. This applies to both the sheltered and the unsheltered exposure environments.

Table 5.1   *Exceptions to expected trends*

Expected trend	Number of comparisons at each depth	Depth (mm)	Porosity	Anhydrous cement content
u<7	10	0–1	–	–
		3–4	–	–
		6–7	–	–
		20–21	–	–
u<s	10	0–1	–	A4 B4 (C4)
		3–4	–	B1 D1 (D4)
		6–7	A4	–
		20–21	A4 C4	–
s<7	10	0–1	D4	–
		3–4	(A1) (A3) (A4)	–
		6–7	A1 A2 B1	–
		20–21	A2 (A1) (C1)	–
CR4<CRl	12	0–1	C7	6/12
		3–4	BS BU CU	4/12
		6–7	A7 AU	6/12
		20–21	A7 AU BU CU	3/12

Notes

For concrete mix and panel details see Table 2.1

u =   Unsheltered exposure for 9 months
s =   Sheltered exposure for 9 months
7 =   7 days old (ie cured but not exposed)
CR1 = Curing regime 1 (ie no additional curing)
CR4 = Curing regime 4 (ie 7 days moist curing).

One explanation of the "concave-down" profiles is that, in both exposure environments, the concrete surface experienced short periods of wetting and long periods of drying. In this way a shallow zone near the surface would exhibit a high degree of hydration due to being regularly wetted, the concrete beneath this would spend most of the time dry and therefore would have a lower degree of hydration and the bulk concrete at still greater depth would be unaffected by the exposure environment and would continue to hydrate as if sealed. This type of exposure was certainly present in the case of the unsheltered panels which were exposed to rain. In the case of the sheltered panels, this would have involved being exposed to cyclic variations in relative humidity with the peaks being sufficient to support hydration (as experienced between December 1997 and March 1998; see Figure A1.2).

Another important feature of the Concrete A profiles is that in many cases (see Figures 5.12 and 5.13 and Table 5.1) the intermediate depth increment porosity values are higher at nine months than at seven days. This is almost certainly a consequence of carbonation. Detailed examination of BSE images of the concrete at different depths shows 3 distinctly different zones, according to the presence of calcium hydroxide or calcium carbonate. In the uncarbonated zone deposits of calcium hydroxide are visible. In the carbonated zone, the calcium hydroxide has disappeared and calcium carbonate is evenly distributed, producing a more uniform and less porous paste. In between the uncarbonated and carbonated zones is the "carbonating zone" in which calcium hydroxide is depleted but an equivalent amount of calcium carbonate is not present; this zone is more porous than the uncarbonated and carbonated zones. Examples of these zones are presented in Figure 5.19.

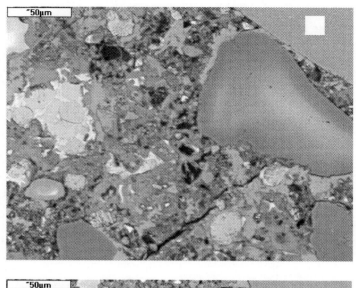

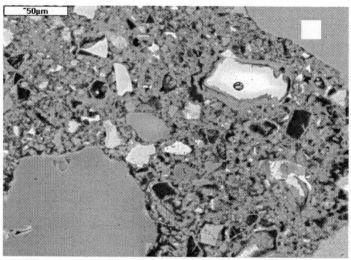

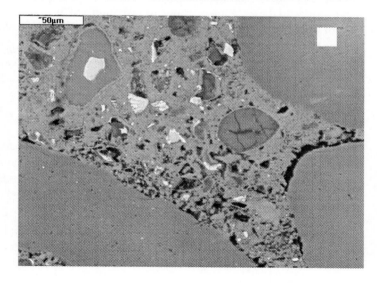

Figure 5.19   *Backscattered electron images of Concrete A1 after nine months of sheltered exposure in the: (top) uncarbonated, (middle) carbonating and (bottom) carbonated zones*

The seven-day moist cured Concrete A surface that was subjected to unsheltered exposure (A4u) showed different behaviour to the other seven-day Concrete A cases. For A4u, the porosity was again lower in the surface few millimetres than in the bulk concrete, but the anhydrous cement content was higher. A possible interpretation is that the density of its originally dense structure was further enhanced by carbonation so as to retard further hydration of the cement.

Concretes B, C and D (Figures 5.8–5.10) showed some evidence of concave-down behaviour, but not to the same extent as Concrete A. In the case of Concrete C and particularly Concrete D, the reduced amounts of calcium hydroxide in the uncarbonated cement paste (due to reaction with the PFA/GGBS) would limit the changes in coarse porosity associated with calcium hydroxide dissolution and calcium carbonate precipitation. In the case of Concrete B and possibly Concretes C and D, the higher penetrability of the concrete would result in the concrete drying to a greater depth during drying cycles and wetting to a greater depth during wetting cycles, thereby smearing the more pronounced behaviour observed for Concrete A.

5.3.4 Effect of curing on nine-month results

In eleven out of 12 cases (four concretes × unexposed (seven days), sheltered (nine months) or unsheltered (nine months) = 12 cases) seven-day moist curing (Regime 4) gave lower porosity at 0.5 mm depth (see Table 5.1) than no curing (Regime 1). Similarly, seven days of moist curing gave lower porosity than no curing in 9/12, 10/12 and 8/12 cases at depth increments of 3.5 mm, 6.5 mm and 20.5 mm respectively.

The anhydrous cement content results show little to no dependence on curing. For example seven days of moist curing gave lower anhydrous cement content than no curing in 6/12, 8/12, 6/12 and 9/12 cases at depth increments of 0.5 mm, 3.5 mm, 6.5 mm and 20.5 mm respectively.

Examination of Figures 5.11–5.14 shows that, after nine months exposure, differences in porosity attributed to the different curing regimes were swamped by differences due to nine months of exposure. In 12 out of 16 cases (four concretes × four depths = 16 cases) concrete subjected to poor curing (Regime 1) and then unsheltered exposure (U) had lower porosity than the same concrete subjected to good curing (Regime 4) and then sheltered exposure (S). Of the four cases that did not show this trend, two showed the opposite trend and two showed no difference. It should be recognised that this finding is strongly associated with the particular conditions to which the concretes were exposed. If the poor curing regime had involved early exposure to lower humidity air, poor curing may have had a greater long-term effect. Similarly, if the sheltered exposure had been at a lower humidity, as would be expected in a normal internal environment in the UK, the effects of initial curing would also be expected to be increased.

5.3.5 Correlation between porosity and anhydrous cement content

Prior to undertaking this SEM work it was anticipated that there would be a strong correlation between the porosity and anhydrous cement content of the cement paste, on the basis that hydration consumes anhydrous cement and the resulting hydration products reduce capillary porosity. However, the finding that curing regime can cause variation in porosity with depth, without a measurable variation in anhydrous cement content (see Sections 5.3.2 and 5.3.4) suggests that the relationship between measured porosity and anhydrous cement content is more complex than expected.

Figures 5.20 and 5.21 show the correlation between porosity and anhydrous cement content at the four depths investigated at seven days and nine months respectively. Trends in the data are not apparent unless concretes are considered individually and so each concrete is assigned a different data point type. It is clear that Concrete D has higher anhydrous cement (OPC + GGBS in this case) content than the other concretes; this has already been discussed (see Section 5.3.1). It is also clear that Concrete B generally has higher porosity and lower anhydrous cement content than Concrete A, which is a direct consequence of its higher water/cement ratio.

The nine-month data (see Figure 5.21) for the greater depths (6.5 mm and 20.5 mm) show that all four concretes individually display an increase in porosity with a reduction in anhydrous cement content. However, this trend is not found in the seven-day data nor in the nearer surface (0.5 mm and 3.5 mm) depth increments.

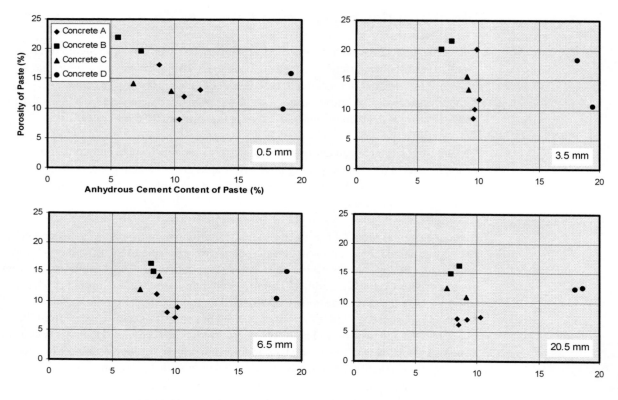

Figure 5.20   *Porosity vs. anhydrous cement content of the cement paste at seven days, as a function of depth*

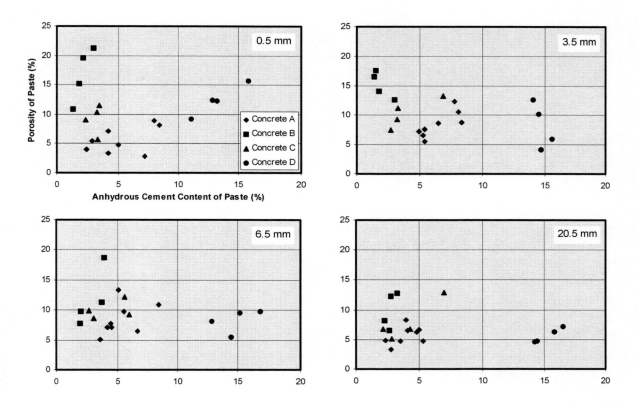

Figure 5.21   *Porosity vs. anhydrous cement content of the cement paste at nine months, as a function of depth*

6 Correlations between abrasion, carbonation and SEM results

One of the objectives of this project (see Section 1.2) was to investigate the relationship between microstructure in the CAZ and durability performance. Hence, in this section, correlations between abrasion, carbonation and SEM results are examined.

Figure 6.1 plots carbonation depth versus abrasion depth. It can be seen that there is a very good correlation (the coefficient of determination, $R^2 = 0.906$), with concretes showing more rapid carbonation having lower resistance to abrasion. The fact that the best-fit straight line passes through the x-axis some distance from the origin (around abrasion resistance = 0.2 mm) suggests that high resistance to carbonation is more easily achieved than high resistance to abrasion.

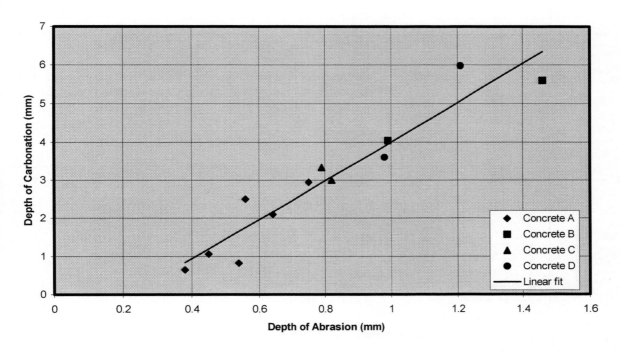

Figure 6.1   *Depth of carbonation vs. depth of abrasion as a function of concrete type*

Figure 6.2 shows the depth of abrasion (nine months) against the nine months' porosity for each of the 4 depth increments. The correlation at 0.5 mm depth is very good ($R^2 = 0.94$), with lower porosity being strongly associated with increased abrasion resistance. As might be expected, the correlation deteriorates with increasing depth, with $R^2 = 0.538$, 0.486 and 0.351 at 3.5 mm, 6.5 mm and 20.5 mm depth, respectively.

Figure 6.3 plots the depth of abrasion against the seven-day porosity, again for each of the four depth increments. The correlation at 0.5 mm depth is moderate ($R^2 = 0.515$), though unsurprisingly, not as good as the correlation based on the porosity measured at the time that the abrasion test was undertaken (ie nine months). Unexpectedly, the correlation at depths of 6.5 mm and 20.5 mm is better than for the nine months' porosity data.

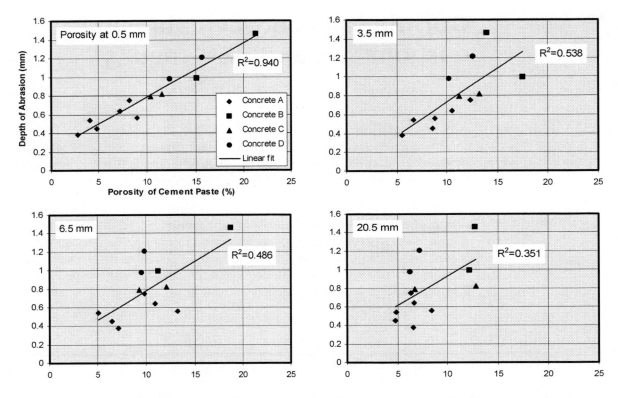

Figure 6.2   *Depth of abrasion at nine months vs. porosity of the cement paste at nine months (at four depth increments) as a function of concrete type*

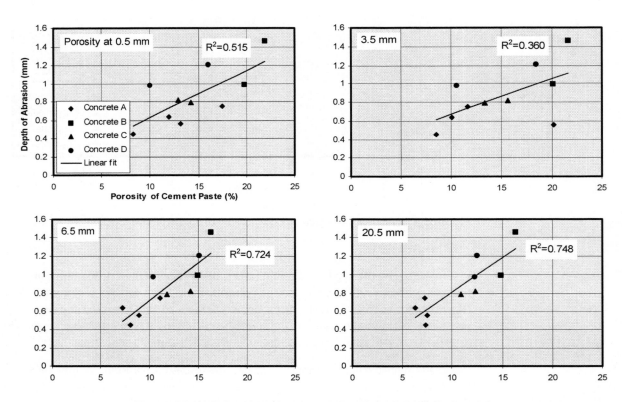

Figure 6.3   *Depth of abrasion at nine months vs. porosity of the cement paste at seven days (at four depth increments) as a function of concrete type*

Figure 6.4 shows the depth of abrasion versus the nine months anhydrous cement content. There is no significant correlation at any of the four depths when the results from the four concretes are considered together. However, some trends are apparent when concretes are considered individually. At least three of the four concretes show increasing abrasion depth with an increase in anhydrous cement content at each of the four depth increments.

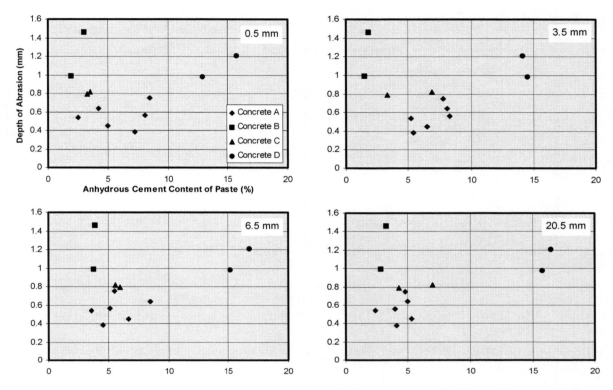

Figure 6.4 *Depth of abrasion at nine months vs. anhydrous cement content of the cement paste at nine months (at four depth increments) as a function of concrete type*

Figure 6.5 presents the depth of carbonation (nine months) plotted against the nine months' porosity. The correlation is good at 0.5 mm depth ($R^2 = 0.770$) and reduces with depth. The 0.5 mm depth in fact represents material from the depth range of 0.40–0.60 mm. Of the 20 cases tested, all had an average carbonation depth deeper than this, ie the 0.5 mm depth porosity results are for carbonated concrete. Both porosity in the CAZ and carbonation depth are dependent on curing, so their correlation and their weakening with depth were expected.

Unlike abrasion resistance, which represents the resistance of the concrete at a moment in time (approximately nine months in this study), carbonation depth represents cumulative behaviour of the concrete over its previous life. Consequently it might be expected that porosity measured at some earlier time could correlate better with carbonation depth measured at nine months than nine months' porosity. Figure 6.6 plots the depth of carbonation versus seven-day porosity. The correlation at 0.5 mm depth is not as good as in the nine months data, but the correlation at greater depths is as good if not better.

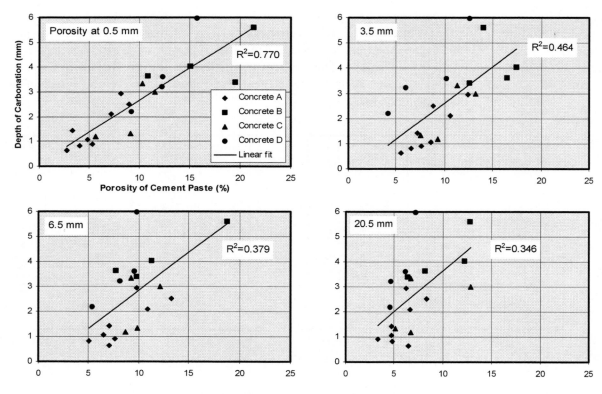

Figure 6.5   *Depth of carbonation at nine months vs. porosity of the cement paste at nine months (at four depth increments) as a function of concrete type*

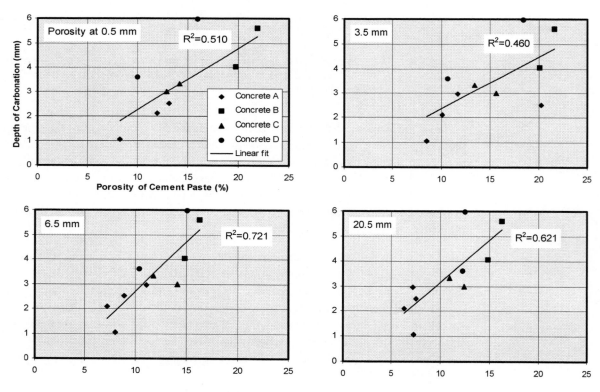

Figure 6.6   *Depth of carbonation at nine months vs. porosity of the cement paste at seven days (at four depth increments) as a function of concrete type*

Figure 6.7 shows the depth of carbonation against the nine months anhydrous cement content. As in Figure 6.4, there is no significant correlation at any of the four depths when the results from the four concretes are considered together, but the individual concretes generally show increasing carbonation depth with an increase in anhydrous cement content at each of the four depth increments.

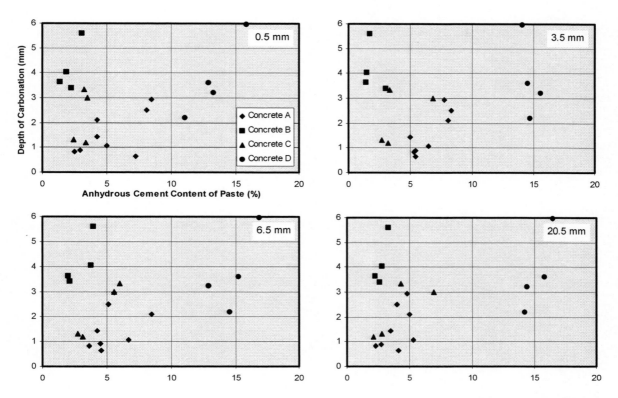

Figure 6.7   *Depth of carbonation at nine months vs. anhydrous cement content of the cement paste at nine months (at four depth increments) as a function of concrete type*

7 Conclusions

7.1 EFFECTS OF PRACTICAL ON-SITE CURING REGIMES ON CONCRETE MICROSTRUCTURE

This project has shown that, at early ages, curing regime can have a significant effect on the pore structure of concrete very near to the cured surface; poor curing results in higher porosity paste near the surface in relation to the bulk concrete.

An unexpected finding was that differences in curing regime resulted in different porosity profiles, but had very little effect on anhydrous cement content. A possible explanation is that at the ambient humidity (around 70–80 per cent RH; see Appendix A1), Curing Regime 1 was sufficient to empty larger capillary pores some distance from cement grains, but not the finer capillary pores closer to the cement grains. Consequently hydration continued, but near the concrete surface the resulting hydration products were formed away from the larger capillary pores detected in the SEM.

Defining the CAZ (CIRIA PR49, Hammersley et al, 1997) as the depth to which the porosity of the cement paste is different from the porosity of the cement paste at depth due to curing, leads to seven-day CAZ depths of 3.5–6.5 mm for Concrete A (Grade 35 OPC) and 6.5–20.5 mm for Concretes C and D (Grade 35 with 25 per cent PFA and 65 per cent GGBS respectively). More porosity measurements at different depths on the same SEM specimens would allow CAZ depths to be defined more accurately.

Benefits gained from curing were found to diminish with long-term exposure, with the effects of nine months of UK exposure (outdoors, unsheltered or sheltered) having a greater influence on microstructure and durability performance than initial curing. This resulted from both further hydration of the cement and carbonation of the concrete and made it impossible to identify the full extent of the CAZ by nine months. (This finding is strongly associated with the particular conditions to which the concretes were exposed. If the poor curing regime had involved early exposure to lower humidity air, poor curing may have had a greater long-term effect. Similarly, if the sheltered exposure had been at a lower humidity, as would be expected in a normal internal environment in the UK, the effects of initial curing would be expected to be greater).

7.2 RELATIONSHIP BETWEEN CONCRETE MICROSTRUCTURE AND DURABILITY

Durability performance has been characterised by measuring abrasion resistance and carbonation depth after nine months of exposure. The results have been compared with the porosity and anhydrous cement content profiles measured in the SEM to investigate the relationship between microstructure in the CAZ and durability performance (see Section 1.2).

Both abrasion and carbonation depth correlated well with porosity measured by SEM (at nine months) in the zone affected (surface few millimetres). Lower porosity was associated with increased abrasion resistance (Figure 6.2) and reduced carbonation depth (Figure 6.5).

The correlations were good despite being based on four different concretes, two of them including PFA or GGBS which are known to produce different pore structures to plain OPC. As expected, the correlation reduced as the depth at which porosity was measured increased.

No correlation was observed between abrasion resistance or carbonation depth and anhydrous cement content when the data from the four concretes tested were considered together. However, when each concrete was viewed on its own the expected trend of increasing abrasion resistance and reducing carbonation depth with reducing anhydrous cement content was usually apparent.

7.3 EFFECTS OF CURING ON DURABILITY

Although not a primary objective, this research has contributed to our understanding of the effects of curing on the carbonation and abrasion resistance of concrete.

Moist curing for seven days produced significantly higher nine-month abrasion resistance than concrete stripped and exposed after 24 hours, even for concrete that was subjected to external unsheltered exposure. This effect of initial curing is expected to reduce with longer exposure (see Section 7.1), but these results confirm the importance of curing in situations where concrete surfaces are exposed to abrasion early in their lives.

Moist curing also enhanced carbonation resistance, based on carbonation depth at nine months, but the influence was less pronounced than for abrasion resistance and is again expected to reduce with longer exposure. In most external exposure environments in the UK and also in relatively humid internal exposure environments, initial curing probably has no significant effect on long-term (say >5 years) carbonation depth.

This research was limited to the deterioration mechanisms of abrasion and carbonation because, based on Phase I (see Section 1.1) of this project, these were expected to be more sensitive to curing than other deterioration mechanisms. It should not be assumed, without direct evidence, that the long-term effect of curing is insignificant for other deterioration mechanisms, nor for drier/less humid exposure conditions than encountered in this study (Appendix A1). Work that would extend our understanding to different deterioration mechanisms and exposure environments is described in Section 8.

7.4 SEM AS A METHOD FOR ASSESSING THE EFFECTS OF CURING

The combination of backscattered electron imaging of polished surfaces in the SEM and greyscale image analysis was confirmed to be a useful method for characterising the microstructure of cement paste. By image analysis separation of the aggregate it proved viable to quantify microstructural gradients in coarse porosity and anhydrous cement content in the cement paste fraction of concrete. As such, the method is of value for assessing the effects of curing. There are other techniques for measuring porosity gradients in cement paste specimens or in concrete specimens (see CIRIA PR49, Hammersley et al, 1997), but these techniques cannot be used to provide porosity profiles in the cement paste fraction of a concrete.

This capability is very important for assessing the effects of curing of concrete as it enables porosity gradients due to the inevitable variation in aggregate content away from a formed surface to be excluded from effects due to curing and exposure. This technique also permits direct examination of the concrete such that any entrapped air voids or micro-cracking are identified and may be taken into account.

The technique only identifies the larger (say > 0.5 μm) capillary pores and does not have the resolution to pick up the finer capillary pores or any of the gel pores. Consequently, the porosity determined by the technique represents only a fraction of the total porosity present. In seven-day old OPC concretes, around 42 per cent of the theoretical capillary porosity was resolved at a free water/cement ratio of 0.70, reducing to around 23 per cent at a free water/cement ratio of 0.55. However, it is the coarser capillary pores that have the most influence on durability. This is supported by the observed correlation between porosity measured in the surface few millimetres of the concrete and both abrasion resistance and carbonation depth after nine months of exposure. If necessary, the resolution can be improved by using a higher magnification, but doubling the magnification requires a four-fold increase in the number of fields imaged and analysed in order to represent the same area of cement paste.

8 Recommendations for further research

8.1 TEST METHOD DEVELOPMENT

(a) Development of a more rapid drying regime to be used prior to resin impregnation of SEM samples to accelerate the process and render the technique more widely applicable. A three-day drying regime would allow results to be produced within seven days of specimens being taken from site.

(b) Comparison of the porosity of cement paste and mortar specimens determined in the SEM with the calculated porosity and the porosity determined using other techniques, with emphasis on the porosity primarily influencing durability.

(c) Measurement of porosity profiles in different locations for nominally similar concrete surfaces to assess the reliability of the method and the effects of different coarse aggregate orientations and large-scale variability in structural elements on the measured results.

8.2 EFFECTS OF CURING ON CONCRETE MICROSTRUCTURE/ DURABILITY

The research outlined below is ultimately aimed at establishing the most efficient way of producing durable concrete on site with particular attention to curing. It would allow guidelines to be established for design/construction which could include "trade-offs" between binder type, water/cement ratio, curing regime and cover depth for different exposure environments. It will enable cover rules and standards to be revised on the basis of improved knowledge and understanding.

(a) More porosity measurements at different depths on the SEM specimens used in this project to more accurately define CAZ depths.

(b) Measurement of porosity profiles on specimens subjected to lower humidity poor curing and lower humidity sheltered exposure conditions than used in this work, to establish how much more important curing regime is under these conditions. This study should involve a wide range of concrete mixes and materials including high strength (with and without microsilica), air entrained and "self-cure" concretes.

(c) "Case studies" whereby core samples are extracted from real structures and examined to establish CAZ depths/microstructure achieved in practical site conditions.

(d) A similar study to the one reported here, but involving different measures of durability performance such as chloride and sulphate profiles and freeze/thaw damage. One aim would be to establish the link between curing and durability, using SEM to help explain the results.

Appendix A1 – Meteorological data

Table A1.1   *Early temperature and relative humidity of sheltered exposure environment*

Date	Time	Temperature (°C)	Relative humidity (%)
21.10.97	09:10	12.1	77
	16:10	14.7	83
22.10.97	13:45	14.6	
	16:00	15.1	73
23.10.97	08:25	10.9	82
	13:15	14.4	
	16:20	14.6	66
24.10.97	08:20	12.1	71
	14:40	12.6	
27.10.97	16:20	13.8	69
28.10.97	08:50	11.3	
29.10.97	16:25	10.7	77
30.10.97	10:00	8.5	80
	17:10	10.3	60
31.10.97	09:30	7.4	69
	16:00	13.5	69
03.11.97	10:25	10.9	91
	16:20	10.8	86
04.11.97	16:15	11.5	85
05.11.97	16:10	13.1	88
06.11.97	16:30	13.2	90
07.11.97	08:10	15.0	
	16:00	13.8	63
10.11.97	16:00	11.4	75
11.11.97	16:20	12.0	79
12.11.97	15:00	13.2	82
13.11.97	16:00	11.2	74
14.11.97	16:20	9.7	86
17.11.97	16:00	15.2	76
18.11.97	15:40	14.3	82
19.11.97	16:00	9.1	86
20.11.97	15:00	12.9	91

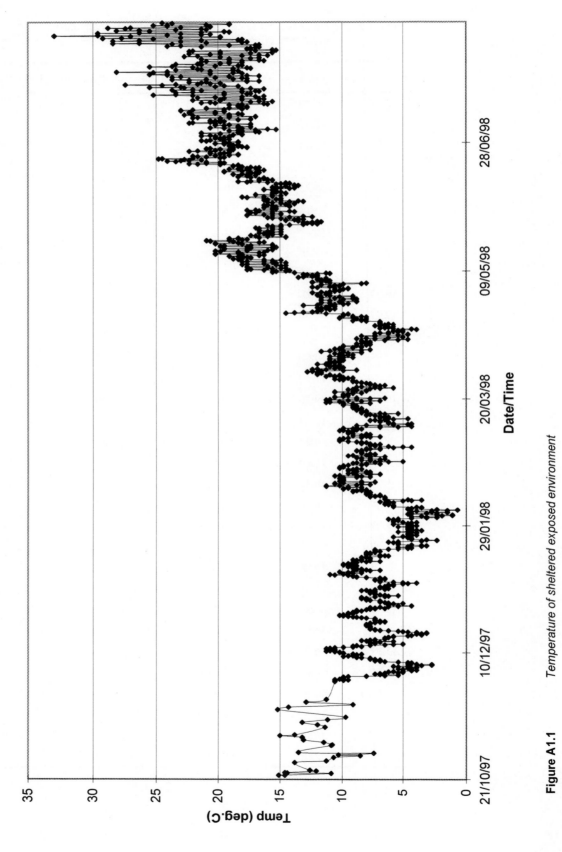

Figure A1.1 *Temperature of sheltered exposed environment*

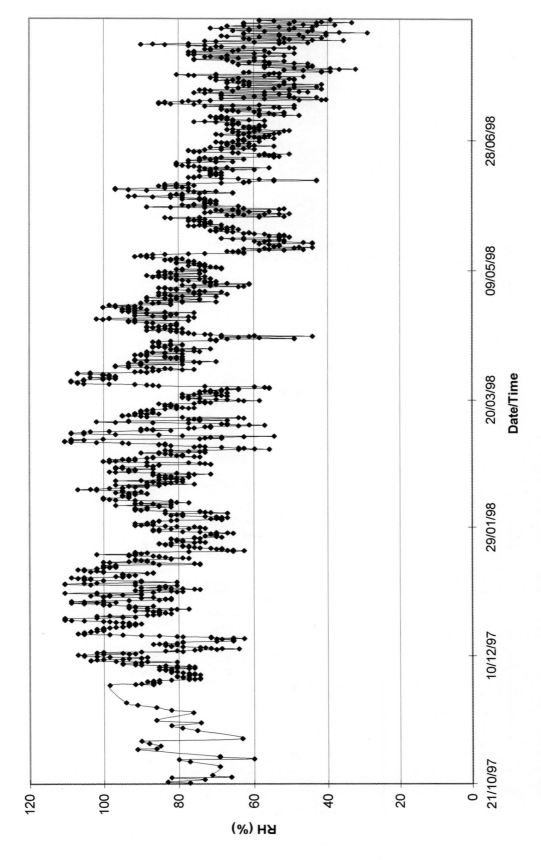

Figure A1.2   *Relative humidity of sheltered exposure environment*

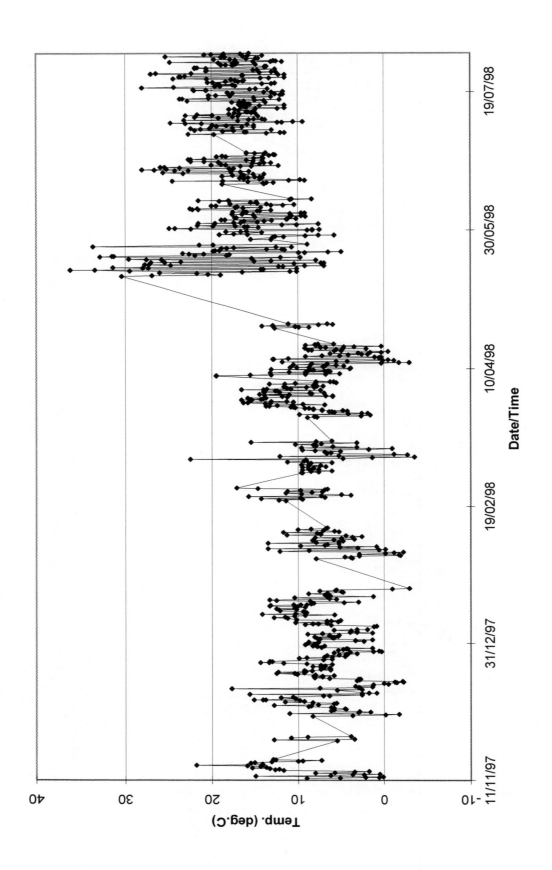

Figure A1.3   Temperature of unsheltered exposed environment

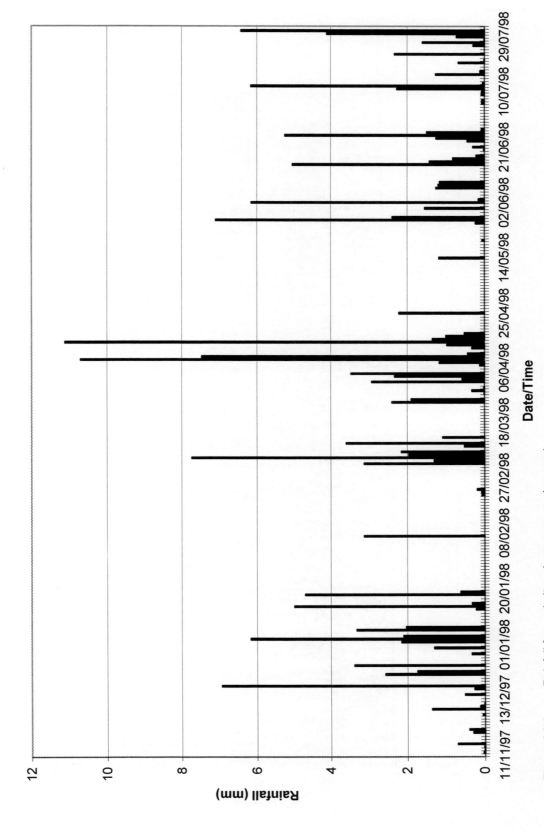

Figure A1.4 *Rainfall for unsheltered exposure environment*

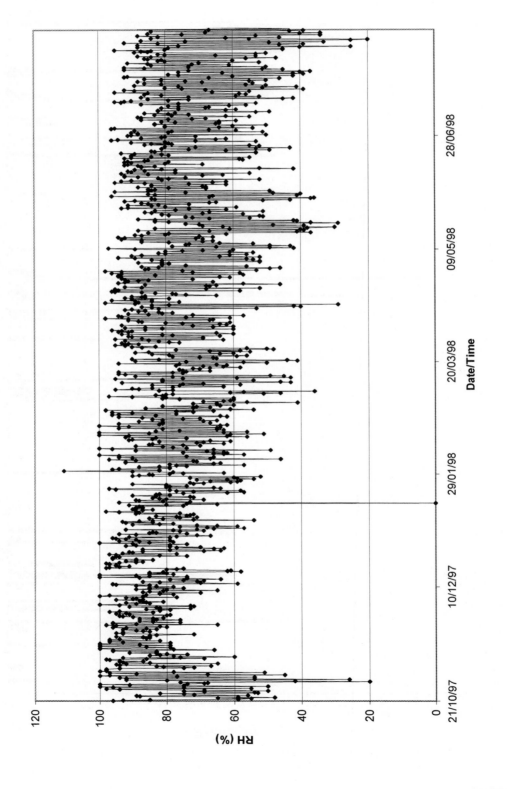

Figure A1.5 *Relative humidity of unsheltered exposure environment*

Appendix A2 – Background to SEM and image analysis

The underlying principle of scanning electron microscopy (SEM) is that a specimen is bombarded with a beam of accelerated electrons which interact with the specimen to produce secondary electrons, backscattered electrons (BSEs) and x-rays. Different detectors are used to collect these signals to provide the information required.

A scanning electron microscope (SEM) consists of an electron gun, condenser lens, specimen stage, and a vacuum system. Electrons are generated by applying a high voltage (2–30 kV) between a tungsten wire filament at the top of the microscope and the specimen stage. The electrons are accelerated down the SEM column. During the journey down the column the electron beam is concentrated by a series of electro-magnetic lenses to make the beam into a probe. A scanning coil directs the electron beam across the sample with the majority of the beam conducted to earth. The inter-action of the electron beam with the specimen is complex. The energy of the incoming electrons is dissipated by scattering over a fairly large volume, typically around 2 μm in depth and diameter for concrete.

Conventional SEMs require the application of a high vacuum in the specimen chamber. Hence concrete specimens must be dried/degassed before examination and, because dry concrete is non-conducting, samples must be given a thin conductive coating to prevent charge build-up on the sample surface. In this study a low vacuum SEM was used; this is a specialised SEM that can operate in low vacuum mode so that undried concrete samples may be examined without the need to apply a conductive coating.

Two types of image can be produced using an SEM, the secondary electron image and the BSE image. The secondary electron image (not used in this project) is generated by the electron beam striking the specimen resulting in the emission of secondary electrons. The contrast of the image is mainly produced by the morphology of the specimen and the technique is usually applied to fractured (not polished) surfaces.

BSE images (used in this project) are formed due to elastic collisions between incident electrons and electrons in the specimen. In the SEM system used in this project the BSEs are detected by a solid state semi conductor device. The scattering of these electrons increases as the atomic number of the material increases, and can therefore reveal difference in composition. Thus the higher the mean atomic number of the phase, the higher the intensity of the BSE signal. On this basis, specific phases within the cement paste and concrete can be determined by the relative intensity of the BSE signal. The intensity of backscattering is also affected by topography, therefore flat polished specimens are essential to obtain a compositional image.

The process of acquiring and processing SEM images involves digitising the electron microscope image signal and storing it as a data array of picture elements (pixels). Each pixel is assigned a value to represent its brightness or grey level in addition to the x and y co-ordinates that define its location. Typical image analysis systems use a numerical scale for levels of grey that ranges from 0 (pure black) to 255 (pure white). Each image comprises 528×384 pixels.

Image analysis may involve the following steps:

- image acquisition
- filtering
- binarisation
- processing
- analysis.

Image acquisition is a simple step of acquiring the image from the SEM to an adequate computer system. The result is a digital image made up of pixels, with a greyscale range ranging from white, through the various shades of grey to black. Typically not all the various shades of grey level (from 0–255) are utilised in an image. Inherent in any digital image is noise, which can be reduced by the process of filtering. Once the grey level thresholds have been established the image can then undergo the procedure of binarisation, where the pixels become either black or white at a particular threshold level, and thus each phase can be successively identified. If necessary, the image can then undergo processing, by cycles of erosion and dilation, to separate features. The image can, after the above procedures have been followed, undergo analysis.

References

BRITISH STANDARDS INSTITUTION (1983)
Testing concrete: method for determination of compressive strength of concrete cubes,
BS 1881: Part 116: 1983
British Standards Institution, London

BRITISH STANDARDS INSTITUTION (1997)
In-situ floorings: code of practice for concrete wearing surfaces, BS 8204: Part 2: 1987
British Standards Institution, London

BUENFELD N R (1997)
"Measuring and modelling transport phenomena in concrete for life prediction
of structures" in *Prediction of concrete durability*, Glanville J and Neville A (eds),
pp 77–90
E&FN Spon, London

BUENFELD N R, HASSANEIN N M and JONES A J (1998)
"An artificial neural network for predicting carbonation depth in concrete structures"
in *Artificial neural networks for civil engineers: advanced features and applications*,
Flood I and Kartam N (eds), pp 77–117
American Society of Civil Engineers, Reston VA

GARBOCZI E J (1995)
"Microstructure and transport properties of concrete" in *Performance criteria for
concrete durability*, Kropp J and Hilsdorf H K (eds), pp 198–212, RILEM Report 12
E&FN Spon, London

HAMMERSLEY G P, SPARKSMAN W G, CLARKE J L, KAY E A,
SLATER D and BUENFELD N R (1997)
On-site curing – influence on the durability of concrete: a review, CIRIA PR49
Construction Industry Research and Information Association, London

KETTLE R J and SADEGZADEH M (1987)
"Field investigations of abrasion resistance" in *Materials and Structures*, 20, pp 96–102
Rilem, Paris

NEVILLE A M (1995)
Properties of concrete, 4th edition, pp 25–31
Longman Group Ltd, London

SADEGZADEH M and KETTLE R J (1988)
"Development of an accelerated abrasion test apparatus with a standardized testing
procedure" in *Materials and Structures*, 21, pp 47–56
Rilem, Paris